HER

Nicola Woods

HarperCollins*Publishers*

The right of Nicola Woods to be identified as the author of this
work has been asserted by her in accordance with the Copyright,
Designs and Patents Act 1988

HarperCollins*Publishers*
Westerhill Road, Bishopbriggs, Glasgow G64 2QT

First published 2002

Reprint 10 9 8 7 6 5 4 3 2 1 0

© Essential Books 2002

All photographs © Len Alden with the following exceptions:

A-Z Botanical Collection: p23, p40, p50, p51, p59, p60, p99,
p106, p120, p122, p134, p136, p152, p159, p1614, p216, p223,
p224/Dorling Kindersley: p30, p74, p108, p110, p125, p129, p141,
p164, p193, p209/Harry Smith: p72, p88, p162, p177, p178,
p208/S & O Mathews: p76, p91, p142, p221

The author and publishers have made every reasonable effort to
contact all copyright holders. Any errors that may have occurred are
inadvertent and anyone who for any reason has not been contacted
is invited to write to the publishers so that a full acknowledgement
may be made in subsequent editions of this work.

ISBN 0 00 712197-0

Printed in Italy by Amadeus S.p.A.

Contents

Introduction

The word 'herb' comes from the Latin *herba*, meaning grass or green plant. Today the word is usually associated with plants for culinary use or that have medicinal value. The word 'spice' is more difficult to define but loosely means an aromatic substance of vegetable origin, often derived from a tropical plant, which has culinary use.

For centuries economies have stood or fallen on their herb and spice production. Their significance was recorded by Elizabethan herbalist and gardener Gerard, and Culpeper, a herbal physician, in their influential publications *Herball* (1597) and *English Physician* (1652).

Historically, herbs and spices have served a number of purposes beyond the culinary and medicinal. The sweet smell of violets was appreciated by our ancestors as a partial solution to their lack of sanitation. Herbs have also informed modern medicine to an extent not always appreciated. Meadowsweet, for example, contains salicylic acid, the main ingredient of aspirin.

Most herbs and spices will grow freely under the right conditions. In northern Europe herbs are tolerant of colder conditions than their more delicate cousins. Guidance is given in this book on creating the right conditions for individual plants.

Interest in the use of herbs and spices is growing, not just for livening up food, but for therapies such as massage and aromatherapy. Each herb and spice featured here has been selected usually, but not exclusively, for its culinary or medicinal value.

> In some instances *spp.* appears after the Latin name for a herb. This indicates that more than one species of that herb is discussed in the text that follows.

HERBS AND SPICES

Alecost
Tanacetum balsamita

Family: Compositae/Asteraceae
Alternative name: costmary
Description: hardy perennial
Ideal habitat: adaptable, temperate climates
Part used: leaf

Alecost is a member of the daisy family and is rich in aromatic oils. It originates from western Asia, and was reported by Culpeper to be in almost every garden. It takes its name from its use in ale and from the Greek word *kostos*, meaning 'spicy'; thus the word alecost means 'spicy herb for ale'.

It is sometimes known as 'the Bible leaf', a description derived from a time when Puritans used the fragrant leaf in the Bible as a bookmark, because the scent was supposed to dispel faintness and hunger during lengthy sermons. Alecost is closely related to **feverfew** and **tansy**.

USES

Culinary: the fresh herb can be added discreetly to meat and vegetable dishes. The dried leaves can be used in teas.

Medicinal: originally used to relieve the pain of childbirth, it has no medicinal use nowadays.

Other: can be used in potpourri, and in beer brewing.

CULTIVATION

- From seed in spring (may take up to two months to germinate).
- By division of the roots in spring or autumn.
- Enjoys a sunny, well-drained, stony soil; will grow in shady areas but may not flower.
- Pest-resistant and therefore useful to plant alongside other herbs that are not so.
- Pick leaves as required.

Allspice
Pimenta dioica

Family: Myrtaceae
Alternative names: Jamaican pepper, pimenta
Description: tender tree
Ideal habitat: tropics
Part used: berry

In the 17th century allspice was used to help preserve fish and meat. Allspice wood was used to make walking sticks, but this was halted in order to preserve the trees for their spices alone.

Allspice gets its name from its aroma, which combines cloves, nutmeg and cinnamon. As the ground spice soon loses its aroma, it is best to buy the spice whole and grind it when required. Most of the flavouring is derived from the husk.

USES

Culinary: Jamaicans make a drink using allspice and rum, called dram. It is also an ingredient of Benedictine and Chartreuse, and is often used in mulled wine. Allspice is found as a sweet spice in many recipes, especially at Christmas. It is also often added to herring in Scandinavian dishes.

Medicinal: the oils derived from the berries and leaves can be used as an antiseptic.

CULTIVATION

- From semi-ripe cuttings in summer.
- Requires a minimum temperature of 15–18 °C (59–64 °F).
- Enjoys sandy soil.
- Can double its normal height in the rainforest.
- Green berries are harvested between July and September. They turn from purple to brown while drying in the sun.
- Trees can live for up to 100 years. They start to produce berries at five to six years of age.

Aloe
Aloe vera

Family: Liliaceae/Aloeaceae
Description: tender ornamental
Ideal habitat: sunny, well-drained soils, tropics
Parts used: sap, occasionally leaf

An ancient plant with succulent leaves identified in early Egyptian paintings. Used as an embalming ingredient, 'bitter aloes' is the name of a purgative drug made from the leaves of several species. Also recorded in Ancient Greek and Chinese medicine, aloe was thought to have been introduced to Europe in the 10th century.

WARNING

Internal use of aloe may alter the effectiveness of prescription medicines, particularly steroids.

It is a bitter herb, thought to control fungal infections as well as to act as an anti-inflammatory promoter of

Aloe (aloe vera)

healing. Medical research suggests that this herb may be of use as a treatment for certain bowel and digestive disorders similar to irritable bowel syndrome.

USES

Medicinal: for chronic constipation and digestive problems. Also used in colonic irrigation. Avoid in pregnancy.
Other: used in cosmetics for skin care.

CULTIVATION

- Rarely sets seeds.
- Usually from offsets of plant that can be removed and grown.
- Requires sandy soil with grit to improve the drainage.
- Only grown as a houseplant in temperate climates.
- Leaves cut from two- to three-year-old plants, drained and used fresh. Can also be evaporated to form crystals.

WARNING

Although aloe can be used externally for burns and scalds, it is wise to seek medical attention for serious burns.

Angelica
Angelica archangelica

Family: Umbelliferae/Apiaceae
Description: short-lived perennial
Ideal habitat: adaptable, temperate climates
Parts used: leaf, stem, root, seed

Angelica was considered one of the most important herbs during the 15th century and is the most widely used tonic in China after ginseng.

The name was thought to be derived from the Greek word *angelos*, meaning messenger, as a monk had a dream in which an angel came to him and told him that the herb would cure the plague. The herb was also thought to safeguard against evil – especially witchcraft.

WARNING

Wild angelica can also be used medicinally, but is easily confused with water hemlock, which is poisonous.

USES

Culinary: used as a flavouring in Benedictine, the stems can also be used with rhubarb. Candied stems are used for cake decoration. The young leaves can be used in salads and the seeds to flavour pastries.

Medicinal: leaves can be crushed and used to help prevent travel-sickness. It has been used for conditions such as catarrh and bronchial problems. Angelica is not recommended for diabetics.

CULTIVATION

- From fresh seed in either autumn or spring; self-seeds very easily.
- Prefers some shade.
- Needs plenty of water.
- The leaves are gathered before flowering. Roots are harvested in autumn.
- Stems can be harvested at any time from second-year growth.
- Requires space and can grow to 1.2–1.5 m (4–5 ft). The flower attracts insects beneficial to the garden.

WARNING

- Large doses first stimulate the nervous system and then paralyse.
- A skin allergen.

Anise
Pimpinella anisum

Family: Umbelliferae
Alternative names: aniseed,
  sweet cumin
Description: half-hardy
Ideal habitat: coastal tropical
  areas
Parts used: leaf, seed, oil

Anise has a particularly delicate and sweet aroma. It is
thought to resemble **fennel** in spiciness, and **liquorice**
in flavour. The seeds are borne on a feather-leafed
plant from the same family as parsley and carrots,
growing up to 60 cm (2 ft) high.

Although native to the eastern Mediterranean, anise
has also been found in southern Russia and the
Americas. The seeds lose their flavour quite quickly, so
it is best to buy in small quantities, grinding them as
required. Dry frying is recommended to bring out the
best flavour. Anise contains the same volatile oils as
fennel, **star anise** and **sweet cicely**.

USES

Culinary: popular addition to alcoholic drinks such as the aperitifs Pernod and Ricard, as well as ouzo and arrack. Also used in spicy dishes and breads, cakes and pastries.

Medicinal: the oil from the seed is used in cough mixtures and throat pastilles. A simple cure for hiccups is to chew the seeds and then swallow them with a glass of water.

Other: can be used in perfumes, but most commonly associated with being attractive to dogs; aniseed trails have been used to draw dogs along a specific route.

CULTIVATION

- From seed in spring.
- Requires sun and rich, well-drained, sandy soil.
- Plants and leaves harvested during summer.
- Seeds collected as they ripen.
- Leaves picked as required.

Anise, Star
Illicium verum

Family: Magnoliaceae
Description: evergreen
  hardy tree
Ideal habitat: acid/neutral
  soils, shaded hot climate
Parts used: fruits, oil

The anise tree, which bears magnolia-like flowers, lives and produces fruit for almost one hundred years. It first bears fruit at six years of age. When picked, the fruits are a rusty red colour. After drying, the seed is used with the husk to produce the ground spice.

The Japanese originally burned the aromatic bark as a form of incense. However, the spice, which has a flavour and aroma similar to **liquorice**, is now very important in Chinese cooking. It is also known to have antibacterial and antifungal effects, and contains the same aromatic oils as **anise**, **fennel** and **sweet cicely**.

USES

Culinary: used in five-spice and for Chinese curries, pickles and sauces.

Medicinal: helps coughs and conditions like lumbago.

Other: sucked by the Chinese as a breath freshener. Used to flavour liqueurs and soft drinks.

CULTIVATION

• Propagate by semi-ripe cuttings.

• Requires shade and moist, drained, slightly acid soil.

• Fruits are picked when ripe.

Annatto
Bixa orellana

Family: Bixaceae
Description: tender evergreen shrub
Ideal habitat: tropical climates
Part used: seed

The seeds of annatto are used for their colourant properties – war paint used by the Central Americans was made from annatto. They also impart a slight nutmeg aroma and have a peppery flavour.

The plant produces heart-shaped fruit, which have spiky hairs to protect them from foraging animals. When ripe, the fruit splits open yielding as many as fifty seeds in its pulp.

USES

Culinary: the orange colouring made from the husk is commonly used as a food colourant, particularly for red cheeses. It is also used to make the brightly coloured Jamaican sauce for salt cod and ackee. The seeds, when cooked with rice, provide a good alternative to saffron.

Medicinal: once used in African countries to control fevers.

Other: used as a natural dye. In India the pulp is used as an insect repellent.

CULTIVATION

- From fresh seed sown in autumn.
- Requires sandy soil.
- From semi-ripe cuttings of young growth.

- Often planted as a hedge.
- Leaves are picked as required.
- The seeds are collected as the fruits ripen.

Arnica
Arnica montana

Family: Compositae/Asteraceae
Alternative name: mountain tobacco
Description: hardy perennial
Ideal habitat: mountainous, temperate regions
Part used: flower

A 'protected' wild plant, the smell of which is enjoyed by bees. However, the smell can also cause sneezing – its name is likely to have been taken from the Greek word *ptarmikos* which means 'sneeze'.

Strangely, arnica is used in Germany to treat heart conditions, but is only allowed in the UK for external application, while in the US it is considered unsafe.

Arnica is both therapeutic and toxic, and the US drug agencies are being ultra-cautious.

USES

Medicinal: only for use by qualified herbal practitioners. It is thought that homeopathic use may be effective against epilepsy and seasickness. May be a stimulant for hair growth.

Other: the leaves and roots have been smoked as a herbal tobacco, which gave it its alternative name of 'mountain tobacco'.

CULTIVATION

- From seeds sown in autumn.
- By root division in spring.
- Requires rich, well-drained, acid soil.
- Leaves are prone to attack by slugs and caterpillars.
- Flowers are picked when fully open and dried for use in creams.

WARNING

May cause skin rash and should not be applied to broken skin.

Asafoetida
Ferula foetida

Family: Umbelliferae
Description: hardy perennial
Ideal habitat: rich, well-drained,
    sunny position
Parts used: stem, root

A member of the carrot family that grows to as much as 3.6 m (12 ft) high in the wild. When raw, the resin or powder – which is derived from the stems and roots – has an unpleasant smell that disappears when added to other ingredients.

USES

Culinary: enhances Indian vegetarian dishes. Its strong onion/garlic properties make it particularly useful to certain Indian religions that prohibit the use of onions and garlic in cooking. Only small amounts of resin are used. Can be obtained in powder form.
Medicinal: thought by some to be a useful antidote to flatulence, hence its use in Indian dishes with pulses.

CULTIVATION

- From seed in late summer.
- Requires rich, well-drained soil.
- Harvested as it flowers, the gum resin is scraped from the roots.
- Resins are formed into lumps and used as required.

Basil
Ocimum basilicum

Family: Labiatae/lamiaceae
Description: tender ornamental
Ideal habitat: Mediterranean climates
Parts used: whole plant, leaf, seed, oil

Basil has a rich and sometimes contradictory history. At one time it was known as the 'kingly herb' and is supposed to have grown around Christ's tomb. In fact it is believed that growing basil above a corpse helps the decaying process. The Greek Orthodox church was also thought to have used it to prepare holy water.

Yet while it was believed to ward off witches, it was also linked with the devil.

Basil is rich in volatile oils, the amount varying with the species and according to growing conditions. Sweet basil was thought to clear the brain, and if a few drops were applied to a sleeve would help relieve mental fatigue.

USES

Culinary: a common ingredient of pesto, and used widely with tomato-based dishes and pasta. To obtain the best flavour the leaves should be gently torn before adding to the dish as the volatile oils are so easily lost.

Medicinal: was used for feverish illnesses and poor digestion, although rarely used in remedies now.

Other: used in aromatherapy as a fortifying oil with a spicy aroma and has a toning effect on the skin. Can be grown in a pot in the kitchen where it acts as a fly repellent; if you crush a leaf and rub it on to the skin it will repel mosquitoes.

CULTIVATION
• From seed in spring.
• Requires sun and rich, light, well-drained soil.

- Maintain temperature above 10 °C (50 °F).
- A good companion plant to tomatoes as it repels insects.
- Susceptible to attack by slugs.
- Use leaves as required.

Bay
Laurus nobilis

Family: Lauraceae
Description: perennial evergreen tree
Ideal habitat: temperate climates
Part used: leaf

Although native to the Mediterranean, bay is a popular hardy ornamental tree steeped in history. The bay wreath was an important symbol, not only at the early Olympics but also for poets and noblemen of the time. Apollo, the Greek god of prophecy, poetry and healing, was reputed to have had his temple roof made of bay leaves to protect him from disease. Large doses of bay can have a narcotic effect.

USES

Culinary: used in bouquet garni, or added to stews, casseroles and desserts.

Medicinal: thought to aid digestion, it was also applied externally to help cure scabies.

Other: bay leaves have been used for packing figs as they help to deter weevils.

CULTIVATION

- From seed in spring.
- From semi-ripe cuttings or suckers in summer.
- By layering in autumn.
- Requires well-drained soil in sun or partial shade.
- Protect from hard winters and strong winds as leaves can be damaged.
- Leaves can be harvested as required and dried, although fresh leaves have a better flavour.
- Can be trimmed into topiary or a standard to provide a formal effect.

Bergamot
Monarda didyma

Family: Labitatae/Laminaceae
Alternative names: bee balm, Oswega tea
Description: hardy perennial
Ideal habitat: temperate woodland areas
Part used: whole plant

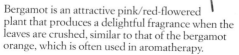

Bergamot is an attractive pink/red-flowered plant that produces a delightful fragrance when the leaves are crushed, similar to that of the bergamot orange, which is often used in aromatherapy.

The plant originally grew around the River Oswego near Lake Ontario. Here the Native Americans used it for its antiseptic properties – it contains thymol, also found in **thyme**. North Americans also made Oswega tea from bergamot. This was used as a replacement for Indian tea following the Boston Tea Party, when American patriots emptied vast amounts of tea from English vessels into Boston Harbour in protest at British tax on tea imported to the colonies.

USES

Culinary: tea can be made from the leaves and added sparingly to salads. Earl Grey tea is flavoured with bergamot. The flowers can also be used in salads.

Medicinal: used as an antiseptic, and for flatulence and nausea.

Other: used in potpourris for its fragrance and the fact that the flowers retain their colour. Used in aromatherapy – when burned the oil acts as a room freshener.

CULTIVATION

- From seed in spring.
- By division of plants in spring.
- By softwood cuttings in early summer.
- Requires shaded, rich, moist soil.
- Mulch in winter to protect the plant.
- Dig up and divide every three years.
- Pick leaves as required.
- Cut flowers will dry well and retain their colour.

Blackcurrant
Ribes nigrum

Family: Grossulariaceae
Alternative name: quincy berry
Description: hardy
Ideal habitat: sunny/shaded, well-drained, temperate regions
Parts used: leaf, fruit

The blackcurrant is most commonly associated with its sweet-sour fruit and the drink made from this. However, in the 16th century it was thought that the fruit bred worms. Later, in the 18th and 19th centuries, the leaves were used as a substitute for tea during shortages. The dried leaves were also used to make Indian tea 'go a little further'.

Blackcurrants are an extremely good source of vitamin C, a fact used to market it as a drink. They are also a very good source of gamma linolenic acid (GLA) (as are **evening primrose** and **borage**), which is extracted and used to help relieve pre-menstrual symptoms. Blackcurrant may benefit eczema.

USES

Culinary: the fruit is used in jams and for desserts.

Medicinal: excellent for colds and sore throats. Helps prevent scurvy and promote good skin. Of benefit to some eczema sufferers.

Other: leaves are used for herb tea and the oil is extracted for medical and cosmetic preparations.

CULTIVATION

- From hardwood cuttings in winter; prefers clay soils.
- Maintain by removing old or weak growth in autumn.
- Replace old bushes every ten years.
- Leaves picked during the growing season.
- Fruits picked when ripe.
- Oil is extracted from the seeds.

Borage
Borago officinalis

Family: Boraginaceae
Description: hardy annual
Ideal habitat: sunny, temperate climate
Parts used: leaf, flower, seed

The name borage is believed to come from the Celtic word *borrach*, meaning 'courage', hence the practice of floating borage flowers in the stirrup cup from which the Crusaders were supposed to have drunk. These days, the stirrup cup is associated with hunting, and traditionally contains the celebratory drink of all those participating.

WARNING

Skin irritant and allergen.

Borage has rough hairy leaves with delightful blue flowers. The seed was thought valuable enough to be taken by the Pilgrim Fathers when they left English shores for America.

USES

Culinary: the hairy leaf tastes a little like cucumber and can be added to drinks and salads.

Medicinal: the oil found in the seeds is rich in gamma linolenic acid (GLA) (*see* **evening primrose**), which has been found to be useful in treating menstrual irregularities and eczema.

Other: the dried flowers add colour to potpourris.

CULTIVATION

- From seed in spring or summer.
- Deadhead to prevent self-seeding. Avoid composting the heads as the seeds will survive.
- Will continue to flower until the first major frost, when the whole plant dies.
- The flowers attract bees.
- Prefers well-drained soil but will tolerate poor soil.
- Leaves should be harvested as the plant flowers and used fresh for infusions.

WARNING

Some countries have legal restrictions on the herb (but not the seed).

Calamint
Calamintha nepeta

Family: Labiatae
Description: hardy perennial
Ideal habitat: sunny, drained,
  lime soils, temperate
Part used: whole plant

Though not a common plant, calamint has been used
for centuries. The small purple-flowered plant has pale
green, downy leaves that produce a delightful aroma.

It has been shown to contain the active ingredient
pulegone (also found in **pennyroyal**), which is known
to cause abortion, hence its early use to expel a dead
child from the womb.

USES

Culinary: the mint-flavoured leaves can be added to
salads.
Medicinal: given to women for menstrual
irregularities, though not advised for pregnant
women. Can be used as a poultice for bruises.

CULTIVATION

- From seed in spring or autumn.
- By softwood cuttings in summer.
- By division of roots in spring.
- Prefers drained to dry, neutral to alkaline soil in sun.
- Harvest in summer for best results.

> **WARNING**
>
> Not suitable for pregnant women.

Camomile
Chamaemelum nobile

Family: Compositae/Asteraceae
Description: hardy evergreen perennial
Ideal habitat: sandy soil, well-drained, temperate regions
Parts used: flower, leaf, oil

The name camomile is derived from the Greek word meaning 'earth apple' or 'apple of the ground', and is a low-growing plant which spreads. It is commonly used for lawns, although it would not withstand the normal wear and tear of traditional lawns. It will repel flying insects when planted next to onions.

In the book by Beatrix Potter, camomile was used by Mrs Rabbit when Peter Rabbit got an upset stomach as a result of eating too many young lettuces from Mr MacGregor's garden.

USES

Culinary: used mainly as a herb tea.

Medicinal: has sedative qualities and is used for insomnia with **hops**, **passion flower** and **valerian**. Used for colic, morning sickness and fevers, and said to be of use in temper tantrums. However, excessive internal consumption is reported to cause vomiting and vertigo. The oil stimulates the uterus and should not be used in pregnancy.

Other: used in beauty preparations and to lighten hair. Used in herb pillows and potpourri.

CULTIVATION

- From seed in spring or autumn.
- By division from older plants in spring.

WARNING

Excessive consumption may cause vomiting.

- Pick flowers when fully open for drying.
- Unlikely to survive in wet or very cold weather.

Capsicum

See **Chillies**

Caraway
Carum carvi

Family: Umbelliferae
Description: hardy biennial
Ideal habitat: warm, temperate climates
Parts used: mainly seed, though leaf, root and oil also used.

Caraway was used by the Romans to flavour the bread eaten by soldiers. The Ancient Egyptians placed caraway in tombs to ward off evil spirits. It also

Capsicum (capsicum annum)

became an important ingredient in love potions. There are even reports of the use of caraway from seeds that were found over 5,000 years ago.

Caraway is a member of the same family as **parsley** and carrot. Its pungent peppery flavour is a result of the high content of carvone (also found in the **mint** family), a volatile oil that constitutes about half of the oil found in the seeds.

USES

Culinary: the seeds are commonly used to flavour cheese, but have also been used for both sweet and savoury dishes, from sauerkraut to coleslaw. They are often used in Jewish cookery. The seeds are particularly popular in Scandinavian drinks such as schnapps. The leaves, which have a flavour somewhere between **dill** and **parsley**, can be used for salads, while the roots can be cooked as a vegetable.

Medicinal: the seeds can be chewed for relief of indigestion and to sweeten the breath, as well as an antidote to flatulence.

Other: used in the perfume industry for its aroma, as well as commercially for flavouring.

CULTIVATION

- From seed in spring or early autumn.
- Colder conditions may prevent seed from ripening in time for harvest.
- Self-seeds but does not like to be transplanted.
- Requires sun and well-drained soil.
- Flowers attract parasitic wasps that feed on aphids.
- Seeds are harvested as they ripen.
- Leaves and roots can be harvested as required.

Cardamom
Elettaria cardamomum

Family: Zingiberaceae
Alternative name: elachi
Description: herbaceous perennial
Ideal habitat: equatorial climates
Parts used: seed, oil

Cardamom is said to have been grown in the ancient gardens of Babylon. The Ancient Egyptians chewed the pod to whiten the teeth and to sweeten the breath. Indian Ayurvedic medicine uses the spice as a slimming aid as it is said to remove fat.

The cardamom pods are carefully dried in the sun, kilns or in hot rooms to prevent them from splitting. Once the pods are split the seeds lose their flavour and aroma. Ground cardamom is rarely available as it loses its flavour so quickly. The seeds of cardamom are removed from the pod by gently crushing them.

USES

Culinary: an essential ingredient in Indian cookery for both savoury and sweet foods. Cardamom is the traditional ingredient of the Indian ice cream kulfi.

Medicinal: it is believed that cardamom cools the body in very high temperatures and aids digestion.

Other: the aphrodisiac properties of the spice have been highlighted in *The Arabian Nights*. The oil is also used in perfumes.

CULTIVATION

- From seed in autumn.
- By division of plants in spring or autumn.
- Requires rich, moist, well-drained soil.

- Minimum temperature of 18 °C (64 °F).

- Bush yields pods after three years and will continue to do so for a further 15 to 20 years.

- Harvesting the pods is very labour-intensive as they have to be hand-picked, since the pods do not ripen at the same time.

- Not normally grown in temperate regions, but can be grown in a container pot for its attractive foliage.

Cassia
Cinnamon cassia

Family: Lauraceae
Description: tender evergreen tree
Ideal habitat: tropical climates
Parts used: bark, bud

The early Chinese and the Egyptians were familiar with cassia; it was even mentioned in the early books of the Bible and in the Psalms.

It is very similar to **cinnamon**, which comes from the same family (although cassia is used for savoury dishes

and **cinnamon** mostly for sweet). Cassia is slightly
more pungent and less fragrant than **cinnamon**, but
both contain camphor.

USES

Culinary: often used for savoury foods, cassia is also
found in Chinese 'five-spice' and is used to flavour
certain types of German chocolate. The buds look
a little like cloves and can be used for pickles.

Medicinal: the oils found in cassia are used in tonics
and are thought to be a cure for sickness and
diarrhoea.

CULTIVATION

- From seed sown under cover.
- By propagation of semi-ripe cuttings in summer.
- Requires moist, well-drained soil in sun or partial shade.
- The outer bark is removed from the trees when chopped down. Inside the greyish outer bark is found the deep brown cassia bark; it curls up as it dries.

- Needs a minimum temperature of 15 °C (59 °F).
- Unripe fruits are picked and dried as cassia buds.

Catmint
Nepeta cataria

Family: Labiatae/Lamiaceae
Alternative name: catnip
Description: hardy perennial
Ideal habitat: temperate,
    sunny/part-shaded, well-drained
    soils
Part used: whole plant

The Roman city of Nepeti is thought to have given its name to the catmint. It has also been known as 'herb cataria' or 'herba catti' due to its attractiveness to cats.

Catmint found favour in the 1960s when it was smoked for its mild hallucinogenic properties. The stimulant responsible for the effect on cats is thought to be similar to **valerian** and is known as actinidine.

Catmint also contains thymol, which is found in **thyme**, citronella, which is found in **lemon balm**, and pulegone, which is found in **pennyroyal** and **calamint.**

USES

Culinary: used for **mint** tea or lemon-flavoured tea.
Medicinal: used for feverish illnesses, insomnia and
    nervous indigestion.
Other: it is most commonly used dried in cat toys. Its
    scent is similar to that of the sex hormones
    produced by cats, so take care when planting this
    in your herb garden.

CULTIVATION

- From seed in spring and summer.
- From softwood cuttings in late spring.
- By division in spring or autumn.
- Enjoys well-drained sunny or part-shaded position.
- Dislikes wet winters.
- Acts as a useful repellent to some vegetable pests.
- Collect leaves and flowering tops when young.

Cayenne

See **Chilli**

Chervil
Anthriscus cerefolium

Family: Umbelliferae/Apiaceae
Description: hardy annual
Ideal habitat: warm,
   temperate climates
Part used: leaf

Chervil was brought to Britain by
the Romans as one of their Lenten herbs and was used
during that period, but in particular on Maundy
Thursday when it was eaten for its restorative and
blood-cleansing properties.

Although thought to be a spring tonic, it is rarely used
as a medicinal herb today, even though it was
considered to be good for poor memory and for
mental depression.

USES

Culinary: an essential ingredient of fines herbes and ravigote, it has a delicate aniseed flavour that deteriorates on drying or with prolonged cooking. Used raw in cooking and as a garnish. Used in small quantities, the leaves enhance the flavour of other herbs.

Medicinal: used to prevent fluid retention and eczema, and has been used externally for inflamed eyelids and conjunctivitis as well as haemorrhoids.

Other: infusions can be used to cleanse the skin, maintain suppleness and to discourage wrinkles.

CULTIVATION

- From seed in spring or late summer for winter harvest.
- Thrives best in semi-shade in a rich, moisture-retentive soil.
- Although hardy, it will need protection in colder areas.
- Does not enjoy hot or dry conditions where it is prone to bolting.

• Use fresh leaves for cooking. The young leaves can be frozen for later use.

Chicory
Cichorium intybus

Family: Compositae/Asteraceae
Alternative name: wild succory
Description: hardy perennial
Ideal habitat: temperate
   climates in open,
   sunny ground
Parts used: leaf, root

The Ancient Egyptians, Greeks and Romans all considered chicory to be an important herb, and the attractive blue flowers were said to represent the eyes of a young girl weeping for her lover.

Chicory is regarded as a 'floral clock', as the flowers open to the sun's rays and close after about five hours, thereby giving some idea of the time of day. The leaves appear to align themselves to the north.

USES

Culinary: useful addition to salads, or can be braised. Once popular as a substitute for coffee, where the root was roasted and then ground.

Medicinal: a tonic like **dandelion**, it was thought to be especially good for gallstones. Its diuretic properties have made it good for treating rheumatism and gout. Used in Ayurvedic medicine.

Other: the blue flowers can be used for making a dye.

CULTIVATION

- From seed in spring or late summer.
- Prefers a light, slightly alkaline, well-prepared soil.
- Will self-seed in suitable conditions.
- Grows tall and prefers the early morning sun.
- Pick leaves when young.
- The roots can be harvested in summer.

WARNING

Damage to the retina may occur if chicory is consumed excessively and continuously.

Chicory (Cichorium intybus)

Chilli
Capsicum annuum

Family: Solanaceae
Description: tender annual
Ideal habitat: hot climates typical of India, Africa and Mexico, although may grow in the Mediterranean
Part used: fruit

Chillies, with their fiery flavours, have been used extensively throughout history as a flavouring to pep up dull foods. Eating foods with added chilli cools the body down on a hot day because the intense heat of the chillies causes sweating so body heat is lost.

The difference in intensity of flavour between different chillies is extremely wide, from the mild sweet pepper, capsicum, popular for its colour, at one end of the scale to the hot jalapeno chilli commonly found in Mexican dishes. In between the two are many other chillies with varying degrees of hotness. It is always wise to treat all chillies as hot unless you know otherwise.

Cayenne is the ground spice of the pepper *Capsicum frutescens*. It is a fine, very hot powder. It was originally grown in the region of Cayenne in French Guyana, although it is now grown in India, Japan and East Africa. It is used very carefully in cooking, owing to its heat.

Paprika (*Capsicum annuum*) is a fine powder made from mild varieties of chilli. It is used mainly for its colour and is the traditional spice of the national dish of Hungary – goulash. It is also popular in Spanish and Portuguese cooking.

WARNING

The oils from chillies can irritate, and it may be best to prepare them under running water, and ensure that you avoid touching your eyes. Thoroughly wash the knife and chopping board to remove traces of the oils. Always wash hands thoroughly after preparing chillies.

USES

Culinary: gives intense heat and flavour to bland foods. Often used to flavour oils and vinegars.
Medicinal: used in the 'cold' stage of fevers, and externally for sprains. The more pungent varieties have antiseptic properties and can irritate the tissues, causing an increase in blood supply that helps to reduce sensitivity to pain.

CULTIVATION

- From seed in spring.
- Requires sun and rich, well-drained soil with a minimum temperature of 18–21 °C (64–70 °F).
- They can be successfully grown in more temperate climates in a greenhouse.
- The fruit is initially green, and as it develops colour so the flavour intensifies. They can be picked ripe or unripe – some chillies are green or purple in colour.

Chives
Allium schoenoprasum

Family: Liliaceae
Description: hardy perennial
Ideal habitat: temperate climates
Parts used: leaf, although flower and bulb can also be used

The Chinese used chives as long ago as 3000 BC, for their mild onion flavour and as an antidote for poison and to staunch bleeding. They became popular in cooking during the Middle Ages when Marco Polo brought them back to the West.

Wild chives were found in Europe, North America and Australia, but it was not until the 16th century that they were grown in gardens for culinary use. Garlic chives, *Allium tuberosum*, are similar to chives but have a white flower and a sweet garlic flavour. Closely related to **garlic** and **wild garlic**.

USES

Culinary: the mild onion flavour of chives is used widely in potato and egg dishes, soft cheeses and in some savoury sauces. The flowers also have a mild onion flavour and can be used as an attractive garnish in salads.

Medicinal: the mildly antiseptic leaves stimulate the appetite and promote digestion.

Other: will prevent blackspot when planted next to roses, and prevent scab when planted next to apples. Also said to prevent scab infection in animals.

CULTIVATION

- From seed in late spring.
- By division of the bulb clumps.

- Requires a rich, well-drained soil in full sun.
- Chives will die down in winter but can survive indoors if kept in a warm, sunny position using a rich compost mix.
- After flowering, chives can be cut right down to the ground to encourage new leaves to shoot.
- The leaves are best used fresh, although they can be refrigerated for up to a week. Freezing is also a suitable option for preservation.

Cinnamon
Cinnamomum zeylanicum

Family: Lauraceae
Description: tender evergreen bush
Ideal habitat: tropical climates
Parts used: bark, leaf

Alongside its close relative, **cassia**, cinnamon is associated with ancient rituals of sacrifice and pleasure. References in the Bible suggest that the spice was more valuable than gold, and the Roman Emperor

Nero was supposed to have burnt a year's supply of
cinnamon at his wife's funeral as a sign of remorse
after killing her in a fit of rage.

Like **cassia**, cinnamon contains camphor.

USES

Culinary: used mainly in sweet dishes, but commonly
added to wines and punches. The sticks are used
to stir hot chocolate and for making Mexican
chocolate. Ground cinnamon is sprinkled over
cappuccinos.

Medicinal: considered an astringent and an antidote
to diarrhoea and upset stomachs. Oil from the
leaves is used as a substitute for **clove** oil.

Other: the oil is used in perfumery.

CULTIVATION

- From seed sown under cover.
- By propagation of semi-ripe cuttings in summer.
- Requires moist, well-drained soil in sun or partial
  shade.
- Needs a minimum temperature of 10 °C (50 °F).
- Harvesting takes place every two years.

- The outer bark is first removed, the inner bark is bruised to help loosen it, long incisions are made and the bark is removed and lifted off for drying.
- The quills are hand-rolled daily until neat.
- Leaves are stripped for distillation of oil.

Cloves
Eugenia caryophyllus

Family: Myrtaceae
Description: tender tree
Ideal habitat: native to Indonesia, though East Africa is the main clove production area
Parts used: flower bud, oil

The name is thought to be derived from the French word *clou*, meaning 'nail', as this describes the appearance of the spice quite well. The trees are very fragrant and their aroma is wonderful.

Originally grown in the Spice Islands in Indonesia, clove trees were traditionally planted to celebrate the birth of a child. If the tree grew well, this was considered a good sign. The child would then wear a necklace of cloves to protect against evil spirits and to give good health.

In 3BC visitors to the Chinese Emperor were expected to suck cloves to sweeten their breath, as it was recognised that cloves were useful in oral hygiene; eugenol, the aromatic oil found in cloves, is an ingredient of today's toothpaste and mouthwash.

USES

Culinary: an ingredient of mixed spice, of the Chinese five-spice, as well as Oriental and Indian cuisine. Also used in pickling spice as well as mulled wine. Especially associated with apples.

Medicinal: a cotton wool bud soaked in oil of cloves helps relieve the pain of toothache.

Other: the oil from cloves is an antiseptic and preservative and used in mouthwashes and toothpaste. Cloves are used to flavour Indian and Indonesian cigarettes.

CULTIVATION

- From seed in spring.
- From semi-ripe cuttings in summer.

- The unopened flower buds are hand-picked when the tree is between six and eight years old to avoid damage to the branches.
- The pink buds slowly change colour until they become the well-known dark brown colour. The cloves are dried naturally as speeding up the drying process produces an inferior product.

Comfrey
Symphytum officinale

Family: Boranginaceae
Alternative names: boneset, knitbone
Description: hardy perennial
Ideal habitat: moist, temperate regions
Parts used: leaf, root

Comfrey was thought to have been brought to England by the Crusaders who were impressed with its healing properties. The secreted mucilage helped to form a firm cast to hold bones in place, hence one of its names

Cloves (eugenia caryophyllus)

– 'knitbone'. It was also made into teas and thought to be a cure for all ills, hence the name 'comfrey', from 'comfy'.

However, it has since been recognised as having carcinogenic properties, but there is also research being undertaken to suggest that it can be beneficial for some conditions.

WARNING

Can cause serious liver damage if taken in large amounts for a prolonged period of time. It is legally restricted in some countries.

USES

Culinary: although comfrey is reported to cause liver damage if consumed regularly for prolonged periods of time, fresh leaves or shoots can be used sparingly for salads and cooking.

Medicinal: contains allantoin and is even a source of vitamin B12, but has been used externally for eczema, sores, varicose veins, ulcers, and sore breasts during lactation. It has also been used as a poultice to cure laminitis (a hoof complaint) in horses.

Other: can be used as a golden fabric dye. The leaves can be used as a good but smelly liquid feed for plants which is high in potassium.

CULTIVATION

- From seed in spring or autumn.
- From root cuttings in spring.
- By division of roots in spring or autumn.
- Prefers sun or shade and moist soil.
- Can be difficult to get rid of if some of the root is left behind.
- Cut leaves as required.

Coriander
Coriandrum sativum

Family: Umbelliferae/Apiaceae
Description: tender annual
Ideal habitat: temperate climates, though not frost-hardy
Parts used: leaf, seed, oil

The seeds of coriander have been cultivated for over 3,000 years and have been found in ancient Egyptian tombs. Coriander is also mentioned in the Old

Testament, and was taken to the New World by the Pilgrim Fathers. It was brought to northern Europe where it was used alongside **cumin** and vinegar to preserve meat.

The Chinese thought it gave them immortality, and it was used during the Middle Ages as a love potion.

USES

Culinary: the seeds are used in curries and in garam masala. The seeds and the leaves, although from the same plant, have different but distinctive aromas. The leaves are a delightful addition to many foods, especially of Oriental and Indian origin.

Medicinal: the bruised seed can be used as a poultice for painful joints. Coriander is thought to be good for the digestive system, reducing flatulence and stimulating the appetite.

Other: the oil is used in perfumes, and as a flavouring in gin, vermouth and Chartreuse.

CULTIVATION

- From seed in spring (and autumn, frost-free areas).
- Requires a light, well-drained soil.

- Stake out as it starts to set seed, as the stems are not strong enough to support the heads.
- The leaves are used when young.
- The seeds are harvested when ripe; it is best to pick before they ripen as they tend to fall out easily.
- It does not do well planted close to fennel.
- Commercially grown coriander is not as aromatic as home-grown.
- If required for its seeds, use a good seed-producing variety. For leaves use a good leaf-producing variety.

Cumin
Cuminum cyminum

Family: Umbelliferae/Apiaceae
Description: half-hardy annual
Ideal habitat: native of eastern Mediterranean
Part used: seed

The Egyptians used cumin over 5,000 years ago. Originally thought of as the spice of both greed and meanness, it then became the symbol of faithfulness. At German weddings the bride and groom would carry cumin to demonstrate their desire to be faithful.

The distinctive aroma of cumin is very popular in cooking and is often combined with **coriander**. If cumin seeds are dry fried before grinding they produce a better flavour. The black seeds have a slightly sweeter flavour than the white seeds.

USES

Culinary: an ingredient in garam masala and curry powders. Also used in Mexican food as well as the more traditional Asian, Middle Eastern and North African dishes.

Medicinal: cumin is considered an appetite stimulant and is used for stomach disorders. It is also used in Ayurvedic medicine.

Other: used in perfume oils.

CULTIVATION

- From seed in spring.
- Requires a well-drained, sunny site.
- Normally the seeds ripen when the plant is about four months old.

- The seeds are a light brown colour, but black seeds are available from Iran. These are slightly smaller and are known as black caraway in India, but should not be confused with **nigella**.

- Seeds are less likely to ripen in colder climates.

Curry plant
Helichrysum italicum

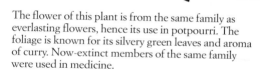

Family: Compositae
Description: hardy evergreen perennial
Ideal habitat: originally from southern Europe, but has adjusted well to the north European climate
Part used: leaf

The flower of this plant is from the same family as everlasting flowers, hence its use in potpourri. The foliage is known for its silvery green leaves and aroma of curry. Now-extinct members of the same family were used in medicine.

USES

Culinary: the smell of the leaf is deceptive as it smells more of curry than it actually tastes, but it is used to flavour rice, vegetables and savoury dishes.
Other: the yellow flowers can be added to potpourri.

CULTIVATION

- From soft cuttings in spring.
- From semi-ripe cuttings in autumn.
- It is difficult to grow from seed.
- Requires sunny, well-drained soil.
- Trim regularly in spring to keep its shape, and again in summer after flowering.
- Protect from frost in very cold winters.
- Pick the leaves at any time.
- Pick the flowers when fully open.
- Some dwarf varieties can be grown in pots.

Dandelion
Taraxacum officinale

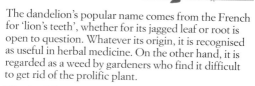

Family: Compositae/Asteraceae
Alternative names: clock flower, lion's teeth
Description: perennial
Ideal habitat: temperate regions
Parts used: leaf, root, flower

The dandelion's popular name comes from the French for 'lion's teeth', whether for its jagged leaf or root is open to question. Whatever its origin, it is recognised as useful in herbal medicine. On the other hand, it is regarded as a weed by gardeners who find it difficult to get rid of the prolific plant.

The dandelion was used by the Arabs in the 11th century, and by the 16th century it was well established in herbal medicine, particularly for its diuretic effects. Referred to by apothecaries as *Herba urinari* and by Culpeper as Piss-a-beds, the names give an indication of its properties.

USES

Culinary: the flowers for wine-making. Leaves can be used for salads and roots for juicing or infusions.

Medicinal: the root is a diuretic. The milky white substance in the leaves and stalks is reputed to be good at removing corns, warts and verrucas. In Chinese medicine it is used for lung and breast tumours, mastitis, abscesses, jaundice, hepatitis and urinary tract infections.

Other: can make a copper-rich herbal fertiliser when leaves are steeped in boiling water and strained after 30 minutes. Use the liquid immediately.

CULTIVATION

- From seed in spring and summer.
- From root cuttings in spring.
- Prefers acid to neutral soil.
- Difficult to eradicate once established and therefore regarded as a weed.
- The flowers should be deadheaded to prevent seeding.
- Pick leaves as required.
- Blanch leaves in autumn to reduce their bitterness by covering with an upturned flowerpot.

Dill
Anethum graveolens

Family: Umbelliferae/Apiaceae
Description: annual
Ideal habitat: dry, sunny, well-drained
   soils, temperate regions
Parts used: leaf, seed, oil

The name dill may have come from the Anglo-Saxon *dylle*, meaning 'to soothe or lull'. The settlers in North America gave it to their children to chew on during long sermons, and it then became known as the 'meeting house seed'. It was also used alongside **vervain** as a protector against demons and diseases.

The herb has a very long history, having been found among Roman remains and also having been mentioned in the Bible. During the Middle Ages the plant was regarded as protection against witchcraft and was used by magicians in their potions. Culpeper records dill as being able to prevent hiccups. Dill's properties and hence market value were well recognised, and as such an ancient Jewish law stated

that a tenth of the crop was to be given to support religious orders.

USES

Culinary: popular in cooking, where it enhances flavours. Particularly popular in Scandinavia in fish, egg and potato dishes. Often added to vinegar and a main ingredient in gravadlax (preserved salmon).

Medicinal: an ingredient of gripe water used for babies. Dill tea or water was used as a remedy for upset stomach and hiccups, and to promote the flow of milk in nursing mothers.

Other: the oil is used in medicines, soaps and detergents. Seeds have been chewed to clear up bad breath.

CULTIVATION

- From seed in spring or summer.
- Regular sowings will provide a steady crop of leaves.
- Requires well-drained, slightly acid soil and sun.
- Will bolt if soil is too dry, so ensure that the site is well-drained.

Dill (peucedanum graveolens)

- Do not grow near **fennel** as it will cross-pollinate and produce hybrids.
- Stake fragile plants to support them.
- Self-seeds easily, so it is best to pick flower heads to prevent rapid spreading.
- Collect seeds by picking flower heads as they begin to ripen. Keep in a polythene bag in a warm place for a week, after which the seeds can be easily separated from their husk.

Elder
Sambucus nigra

Family: Caprifoliaceae
Alternative name: elderberry
Description: deciduous hardy perennial
Ideal habitat: temperate regions
Parts used: leaf, bark, flower, fruit

The use of elder dates from Ancient Greek times. The stems, which are hollow, would have been used to make musical pipes. If placed on a fire, the stems were supposed to provide visions of the devil, hence superstitions such as not using the wood as cradle rockers for babies. However, it was thought that it was lucky to plant elder outside the door as the spirit of the tree would protect the home and its owners from evil.

The anti-inflammatory flavanoid rutin in elder reduces the fragility of capillaries. However, the leaves can be toxic, so great care should be taken with this plant. Its close relative *Sambucus ebulus* is even more toxic.

USES

Culinary: elderflower fritters can be made by dipping the flower head in batter and deep frying. However, it is more common to make elderflower jellies and cordials, which benefit from its sweet, grape-like flavour. The berries can be made into jam, though both the elderflower and elderberry have traditionally been used to make wine, and in the case of the flowers, champagne.

Medicinal: the bark and leaves have been used for chilblains and burns. The flowers and the fruits have been used for flu, colds and other feverish illnesses.

Other: the berries can be used as a purple dye. The flowers have been used for skin lotions, supposed to soften and whiten the skin and remove freckles.

CULTIVATION

- From seed in spring.
- From softwood cuttings in summer.
- From hardwood cuttings in winter.
- Tolerates moist soils, but prefers chalky conditions and sun.
- Easy to grow, but should be cut back to prevent it from taking over from the other plants.
- Flowers should be picked carefully to prevent bruising.
- The berries are picked in autumn when ripe.

Evening primrose
Oenothera biennis

Family: Onagraceae
Description: hardy perennial
Ideal habitat: prefers sun, temperate regions
Part used: seed oil

The evening primrose plant is not especially attractive by day. However, at night-time, when the flowers open, it is noticeably fragrant and its flowers become almost phosphorescent. Towards the end of the summer they remain open all day long.

Ancient herbalists thought that this herb dispelled the effects of wine. It has been used for both cooking and as a medicine, and is becoming recognised as being effective for a number of conditions.

USES

Culinary: the roots can be boiled – they have a taste similar to parsnips.

Medicinal: evening primrose oil is rich in gamma linolenic acid (GLA), an essential fatty acid, which has been found to be beneficial to women who have menstrual problems. Some types of eczema respond to evening primrose oil. Further research is being undertaken to help establish roles for this interesting herb. **Blackcurrant** and **borage** are also rich in GLA.

Other: used for cosmetics. The leaves can be made into an infusion and used in an astringent steam facial.

CULTIVATION

- From seed in spring.
- Deadhead to prevent self-seeding.
- Dig up roots after second year of growth.
- Grows to 90–120 cm (3–4 ft).
- Self-seeds very easily.
- Tolerant plant, but prefers sunny, well-drained soil.
- Use fresh leaves as required.

Fennel
Foeniculum vulgare

Family: Umbelliferae/Apiaceae
Description: hardy perennial
Ideal habitat: temperate regions
Parts used: leaf, stem, root, seed, oil

Fennel was used as an early slimming aid by Roman women as it was supposed to prevent pangs of hunger. It was also used alongside **dill** to chew upon when listening to long sermons in church.

Culpeper sang its praises as a cure for poison caused by snakebites and mushrooms. However, it was its fragrance which was important as it was mainly used to flavour food in the 16th century. It was also used as an insect repellent. It contains the same volatile oils as **anise**, **star anise** and **sweet cicely**.

USES

Culinary: the root can be cooked and eaten as a vegetable, the seeds used in sauces – especially with poultry, lamb and fish – and soups, and the leaves can be used in salads.

Medicinal: used for indigestion and colic, the root has been used for urinary disorders. Also used for mouthwash and gargles for gum disease and sore throats.

Other: used for facials and steam baths for deep cleansing. Also produces a yellow dye. Keeps whitefly at bay by attracting hoverflies and other parasitic wasps.

CULTIVATION

- From seed in spring and autumn.
- By root division in autumn in light, sandy soils only.
- Self-seeds easily.
- Enjoys sunny, fertile, well-drained position.
- Although hardy, does not grow well where there are cold, damp winters.
- Collect ripe seeds for sowing or for culinary use.
- Dig up the root when mature.

Fenugreek
Trigonella foenum-graecum

Family: Leguminosae/Papilionaceae
Description: annual
Ideal habitat: well-drained, fertile, sunny climates
Parts used: leaf, seed

Fenugreek was used by the Ancient Egyptians for embalming and for incense, and during the Middle Ages as a cure for baldness. The Romans used it to feed their animals, and this practice still continues in India. Additionally, the plant is a good source of nitrogen and is therefore a natural fertiliser for the soil.

The whole plant is highly aromatic, smelling of curry powder, but of current interest is the fact that one of its alkaloids, trigonelline, may have a role in cancer therapy. The saponins also present are extracted for use in oral contraceptives.

USES

Culinary: the dried leaves are used extensively in Indian cookery. The seeds can be sprouted for salads, but more traditionally they are used in curry spices. They should be dry fried to reduce the bitterness.

Medicinal: used in Chinese medicine for kidney disorders, and in Ayurvedic medicine to treat digestive complaints as well as gout and arthritis. Has been used to treat diabetes by traditional herbalists, and is thought to be good for digestion in general.

Other: seed extracts used for synthetic maple syrup, vanilla and caramel flavouring.

CULTIVATION

- From seed in spring.
- Leaves are picked as required.
- Seeds are harvested from the pods when ripe.
- Requires fertile, well-drained soil.
- Not grown in northern temperate regions.

Feverfew
Tanacetum parthenium

Family: Compositae/Asteraceae
Description: hardy perennial
Ideal habitat: sunny, dry,
   temperate regions
Part used: whole plant

Although this herb has the name feverfew, there is little evidence to suggest that it has ever been used for treating fevers. Its main claim to fame is in the treatment of headaches. In the late 18th century it was thought to be a particularly good remedy for those who had consumed too much opium.

Feverfew is very closely related to **alecost** and **tansy**.

USES

Culinary: used sparingly in salads as the leaves are bitter.

Medicinal: said to overcome melancholy and soothe headaches. The latter use found fame when research in the 1970s established that feverfew did indeed help reduce migraines.

Other: a mild disinfectant, the leaves are also good for making home-made mothballs. Containing pyrethrins that are harmless to mammals but are an effective insecticide, feverfew is also used as a treatment for head lice.

CULTIVATION

- From seed in spring.
- By division of roots in autumn.
- Enjoys a sunny, well-drained, stony soil; will grow in shady areas but may not flower.

WARNING

Mouth ulceration may occur as a side effect of taking feverfew.

- Pick leaves before the plant flowers.
- Pick flowers before they open and dry hanging upside down.
- Can be invasive.
- Golden varieties are often used as an edging plant in formal herb gardens.

Galangal
Languas galanga

Family: Zingiberaceae
Alternative name: Siamese ginger
Description: tender
Ideal habitat: tropical regions, native of India and Southeast Asia
Part used: root

Galangal, also referred to as greater galangal, was used in the Middle Ages as a medicine and spice and also as an aphrodisiac. It is only recently that it has been more common in Europe. It has a pine-like aroma with similar flavour.

Languas officinarum (lesser galangal) is less common and has a stronger, more peppery flavour and a more fibrous texture.

USES

Culinary: used especially in Southeast Asian dishes with chicken and seafood. Thai soups commonly include slices of galangal, hence its other common name – 'Siamese ginger'.

CULTIVATION

- Propagated by division of its roots.
- Requires sunny, well-drained, rich soil.
- Likes high humidity and frost-free conditions.
- Grows to 1.8 m (6 ft) with elegant, blade-like leaves.
- Roots are harvested during the growing season; late harvesting is more likely to produce fibrous roots.
- Not normally grown in temperate regions, but can be grown in a container pot, predominantly for its attractive foliage rather than its roots.

Garlic
Allium sativum

Family: Liliaceae
Description: hardy perennial
Ideal habitat: adaptable, but originated in India and Central Asia
Part used: bulb

There are many myths and legends surrounding garlic: the Egyptians used it as a medicine; Roman soldiers were given garlic cloves daily to maintain their energy; even in rural New Mexico garlic is said to rid young girls of their unwanted boyfriends – possibly due to the distinctive aroma on the breath when garlic is eaten. During World War I, moss soaked in garlic juice was used as an antiseptic dressing for wounds.

Its very close relative **wild garlic** (*Allium ursinum*) has similar properties to garlic, and its leaves can be used for salads. It is also closely related to **chives**.

USES

Culinary: an ingredient of many traditional dishes, although it is used raw in aïoli (Spain and southern France) and skordalia (a Greek sauce made with walnuts, almonds and olive oil). Can be used in many ways: tuck cloves into slits of lamb joints for roasting; eat whole roasted (the longer it is cooked, the milder the flavour); chop finely and blend with butter for garlic butter; add to vinaigrette dressing to enhance the flavour. Chew cardamom seeds to help dispel the smell of garlic on the breath.

Medicinal: there are many health claims, but it has been used to help prevent infections and treat colds. Applied to the skin, it is said to help treat acne and fungal infections. Its greatest claim is to help in heart disease where it is thought to slow the development of the disease. It also aids glucose metabolism in diabetes, and is used in Ayurvedic medicine.

Other: the juice acts as an insect repellent. An old tale suggests that it cured whooping cough if it was put into the shoe of the wearer.

CULTIVATION

- Tradition holds that planting should be on the shortest day of the year and harvest on the longest.

- Plant cloves in early spring for harvest in summer.
- Plant cloves in autumn, protecting them in winter if very severe.
- Water well.
- Requires full sun in rich, light, well-drained soil.
- As they mature the leaves start to turn brown. They should then be eased out of the ground.
- The garlic should be allowed to dry before being stored plaited or in a string bag in a cool, airy place.

Garlic, Wild
Allium ursinum

Family: Liliaceae
Alternative names: bear's garlic, devil's posy, onion flower, ramsomes, stinkplant, wood garlic
Description: hardy perennial
Ideal habitat: moist, semi-shaded, temperate climate
Parts used: flower, leaf, whole plant

Wild garlic is also known as stinkplant, which aptly describes its pungency. The smell that characterises all plants in this group is due to the sulphur compounds found in them, which are believed to have a beneficial effect on the circulatory system. It is thought to be their smell that keeps them free of disease and insects.

Related to **garlic** and **chives**, this plant is at home in wetter areas and can easily become invasive. It is native to Britain and other northern European countries.

USES

Culinary: leaves can be used in salads and soups, or it can be cooked as a vegetable.

Medicinal: used internally to help reduce high blood pressure and for diseases of the circulatory system.

Other: once used as a household disinfectant.

CULTIVATION

- From seed in spring and autumn.
- By division of plants in summer.
- Prefers moist, semi-shaded areas.
- Pick as required from spring onwards.

Geranium, Scented
Pelargonium sp.

Family: Geraniaceae
Description: tender perennials in temperate regions
Ideal habitat: native to South Africa, but popular in temperate regions
Parts used: leaf and oil, although the whole plant can be used in some instances

Geranium is popular and widely used in South Africa where it is a hardy plant. It was popular in Britain in Victorian times, when it became a houseplant due to its inability to withstand frosts.

WARNING

Pelargonium crispum should not be used in cooking as it may upset the stomach.

There are many varieties of scented geranium, containing numerous volatile oils. These give rise to distinctive fragrances, some of which act as insect repellents, and others of which are used in perfumery.

Scented geranium (pelargonium sp.)

USES

Culinary: used to flavour foods before the advent of artificial flavourings in Victorian times; typically added to cake tins or to make teas and punches. Today, some varieties are still used for food flavouring.

Medicinal: used in southern Africa (Pelargonium quercifolium) for rheumatism, high blood pressure and heart disease, but not reported as being used elsewhere.

Other: popular in aromatherapy as a massage oil and for burning, the oil or leaves can also be added to the bath for fragrance, cleansing and refreshment.

CULTIVATION

• Propagated by softwood cuttings.
• Can be grown from seed, but can be quite difficult.
• Requires well-drained, neutral to alkaline soil.
• Does not withstand frost.
• Pick leaves as required.
• Collect seeds before they ripen (as the pod ripens they scatter the seeds so save the seed pods in a bag).
• Commonly grown in pots and brought indoors to overwinter.

Ginger
Zingiber officinale

Family: Zingiberaceae
Alternative names: adrak, gin, jeung, khing and shoga
Description: tender
Ideal habitat: tropical regions; mainly grown in Jamaica and Asia
Part used: root

In Roman times, ginger was so popular for both cooking and medicine that it became taxable. It has also long been popular in Chinese and Ayurvedic medicine, and is known as 'universal medicine'.

WARNING

Ginger may increase the risk of bleeding if you are taking blood-thinning products.

The ginger root is very portable, meaning it could be carried to different parts of the world where it became as popular as **pepper**. There are several gingers in the family – a close relative known as *Zingiber zerumbet* contains a compound that is used to treat cancer in China.

USES

Culinary: added to a wide range of food and drink,
from curries and chutneys to cakes and biscuits,
and popular in beverages such as ginger beers,
wines and ales. The root can be preserved in
syrup, candied or crystallised, making it a
traditional treat for Christmas time. In China,
ginger is pickled and served as an appetiser, and is
also used in Chinese cuisine.

Medicinal: popular as a cure against nausea and used
to help with morning sickness in pregnancy. It is
also used in Chinese medicine for a variety of
problems, including colds, diarrhoea, shock,
stomach upsets and bronchitis.

Other: used in aromatherapy for relaxing the muscles
in massage, and in perfumes.

CULTIVATION

- By division of roots in spring.
- Requires well-drained, rich soil.
- Requires humid, sunny or semi-shaded conditions.
- Usually treated as an annual crop.
- Roots should be lifted during the growing season
  before they become fibrous.

- The roots will keep well in a cool, dry place, although they are often dried and sold as a powder.
- The powder is hotter than the original root due to a change in some of its volatile oils when ground.
- Not normally grown in temperate regions, but can be grown in a container pot, predominantly for its attractive foliage rather than its roots.

Heartsease
Viola tricolor

Family: Violaceae
Alternative name: wild pansy
Description: hardy perennial
Ideal habitat: native to Europe and North America
Part used: whole plant

Heartsease is one of several species of the viola family with romantic connections, as shown in its old common names 'Love in Idleness', 'Kiss Me Behind the Garden Gate', 'Kiss Me Love' and 'Kiss Me

Quick'. However, it took on symbolic connotations due to its flower colouring, with purple for memories, white for loving thoughts, and yellow for souvenirs.

The **violet** (sweet violet) is a very close relative popular for its perfume.

USES

Culinary: flowers can be added to salads and garnishes.

Medicinal: an infusion of flowers was thought to cure a broken heart, hence its name. However, it has also been used for skin complaints and for urinary problems. Herbalists use it for the treatment of gout and rheumatoid arthritis.

Other: used for skin cleansing.

CULTIVATION

- From seed in spring or autumn.
- From semi-ripe cuttings in spring.
- Requires well-drained soil.
- Harvest flowers throughout the season.
- Deadhead to prolong the flowering period.
- Suitable for growing as a pot plant.

Honeysuckle
Lonicera caprifolium

Family: Caprifoliaceae
Alternative names: beerbind,
    bindweed, evening pride,
    fairy trumpets, honeybind, Irish vine,
    sweet suckle, trumpet flowers,
    woodbind, woodbine
Description: hardy perennial
Ideal habitat: temperate regions
Parts used: flower, stem

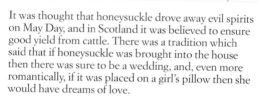

It was thought that honeysuckle drove away evil spirits on May Day, and in Scotland it was believed to ensure good yield from cattle. There was a tradition which said that if honeysuckle was brought into the house then there was sure to be a wedding, and, even more romantically, if it was placed on a girl's pillow then she would have dreams of love.

The plant grows wild in hedgerows and is notorious for climbing up trees and hedges, binding them as it grows. From this its old common name 'woodbine' was derived; the name 'honeysuckle' came from honey bees, which take sweet nectar from the flowers.

USES

Culinary: add flowers to salads.

Medicinal: used for treating coughs and other respiratory tract infections. May have value in helping to treat colitis.

Other: used in potpourri; select the flowers as they are beginning to open as they then have the strongest scent (before the nectar has been collected).

CULTIVATION

- From seed in autumn, allowing to overwinter.

- From softwood cuttings in summer, placing them in well-drained compost.

- Layering: simply bury a stem lightly under the soil, pegging it down if necessary (either in spring or autumn). When rooted (next season) it can be cut from its parent and grown in the desired spot.

- Prune back in spring and after flowering to maintain its shape and to prevent it from growing out of control.

- Pick flowers for salads as required. The palest flowers have the best flavour because they still contain nectar.

Hops
Humulus lupulus

Family: Cannabaceae
Alternative names: hop vine, hopbind
Description: hardy perennial
Ideal habitat: northern temperate zones
Parts used: leaf, shoot, female flower (hops), male flower, oil

Long before hops were used in beer-making the plant was used as a vegetable. Hops originally grew wild, but eventually they were used to replace **alecost** in ale-making. It was originally thought that hops would spoil the taste of ale, and during the reign of Henry VIII attempts were made by parliament to get hops banned. Fortunately for the beer drinkers of today, this did not happen.

Due to the known sedative effect of hops, they have been used to make a tea or more commonly to make a hop pillow.

USES

Culinary: side shoots removed in early spring can be cooked and eaten like asparagus. Male flowers can be used in salads.

Medicinal: help with insomnia and to cure nervous diarrhoea. Used externally for skin conditions such as eczema, herpes and leg ulcers. Can also be combined with **camomile, passionflower** and **valerian** as a sedative.

Other: hops are used as flavouring in beer, while the oil can be used in food and soft drink flavourings. Spent hops can be used as garden mulch.

CULTIVATION

WARNING

Pollen may cause contact dermatitis. Has a sedative effect.

- Sow seed in summer or autumn and leave to over-winter for germination – which can be erratic – and transplant when big enough to handle. Seed may be female or male; until hops grow you will not know the gender. Male flowers are small and grow in branched clusters; females are larger with a soft, pale green leaf.

- Softwood cuttings from female or male plants can be taken in early spring or summer.

- Roots can be divided.

- Requires moist, well-drained soil.
- Can be grown in a large container if supported.
- Pick side shoots in spring.
- Pick male flowers as required.
- Pick female flowers in early autumn, dry and use within a few months as the flavour deteriorates.
- Seeds from wild hops should not be grown near commercial sites as they may contaminate the crop.

Horseradish
Armoracia lapathifolia

Family: Cruciferae
Alternative name: red cole
Description: hardy perennial
Ideal habitat: very adaptable, temperate climate
Parts used: leaf, root

Although originally a medicinal herb, horseradish has a culinary use and is most commonly eaten in the UK with roast beef, and in Scandinavia with fish.

WARNING

Avoid regular consumption if you are pregnant or suffer from kidney problems.

It has a strong radish flavour from where it derives its name ('horse' meaning strong or coarse). However, if grated it releases its volatile oils which then reduce if cooked.

USES

Culinary: the root is used for sauces and accompaniments for meat and fish. The leaves are milder and can be used for salads.

Medicinal: has antibiotic properties and can be used as a poultice for infected wounds and chilblains. Also used to treat gout, arthritis and respiratory infections.

Other: improves disease resistance in potatoes if grown close to the crop.

CULTIVATION

- From seed in spring.
- By division of roots.
- From root cuttings.
- Pick leaves when young.

WARNING

Avoid if you have an under-active thyroid or if taking thryoxine.

- The roots can be used at any time or they can be stored in sand in a cool, dark place.
- The plant is very invasive once established and may take over other parts of the garden.

Hyssop
Hyssopus officinalis

Family: Labiatae/Lamiaceae
Description: hardy perennial
Ideal habitat: dry, sunny position
Parts used: whole plant, leaf, flower, oil

Hyssop is a pleasantly aromatic herb with a long history; there is reference to it in the Bible. It is native to the Mediterranean, where it can often be found on dry banks or old walls.

The volatile oil found in hyssop was used as a lotion by the Persians to give a good colour to their skin. It was recommended by Hippocrates for chest complaints and is still used by herbalists today. Interestingly, the leaf may have antibiotic properties – lepers originally bathed in hyssop – but the leaf also grows a mould that produces penicillin.

USES

Culinary: use flowers in salads. The leaves are slightly bitter but are used in some savoury dishes.

Medicinal: used internally for bronchial conditions; externally it can be applied to bruises and burns. Folklore suggests that it was used for rheumatism.

Other: used as an ingredient in the liqueur Chartreuse. Deters white flies from cabbages, but if planted next to vines it will increase the yield.

CULTIVATION

- From seeds in spring.
- From softwood cuttings in summer.
- Thrives in sunny, well-drained soil.
- Maintain size and shape by trimming.

WARNING

Excessive use of the oil may cause epileptic fits and death. Should not be used in aromatherapy for people with a nervous disposition. Do not use during pregnancy.

- Deadhead to maintain flowering.
- Cut back in autumn.
- Pick leaves and flowers in summer.
- The scent of the flowers improves with drying.

Jasmine
Jasminum officinalis

Family: Oleaceae
Description: hardy
Ideal habitat: sunny, well-drained soils, temperate regions
Parts used: flower, oil

There are several jasmines, of which *Jasminum officinalis* is the most common. It was introduced during the 16th century for use as a perfume oil.

Jasmine is a very potent herb. Originally, odourless oils were used to take up the scent of the jasmine flower to produce the oils. Jasmine teas may not actually contain

jasmine – it is simply good enough for loose leaf tea to be stored alongside the flowers for a few weeks for it to take up the scent. Typically, *Jasminum sambac*, an Arabian jasmine, is used for that purpose.

USES

Culinary: as a food flavouring, especially for maraschino cherries.
Medicinal: used mainly in aromatherapy where the floral scent is said to have an uplifting and relaxing effect.
Other: used in the perfume industry.

CULTIVATION

- From seed in spring.
- From softwood cuttings in summer.
- Can be propagated easily from root layering in summer.
- Requires rich, well-drained soil.
- Pick fresh flowers in the morning just after they open.

Jasmine (jasminum officinalis)

Juniper
Juniperus communis

Family: Cupressaceae
Description: evergreen conifer
Ideal habitat: adaptable, temperate regions
Parts used: berry, oil

Though native to the Mediterranean, juniper is found in climates as diverse as those of the Arctic and the Himalayas. However, it prefers open heaths, moorland and mountain slopes. The bitter aromatic herb has antiseptic properties and was used by the Ancient Greeks to cure snakebites and to help protect against the plague.

It is best known as an ingredient of gin. 'Gin' is the shortened form of the Dutch word *genever*, which in turn is derived from the Latin name for the berry, *juniperus*.

USES

Culinary: an important flavouring, the crushed berries are used in pickles, sauerkraut, game and pâté.

Medicinal: used for cystitis, rheumatism and gout. Steam inhalations were thought to be excellent for coughs and nasal problems.

Other: the oil is used in aromatherapy and for skin preparations. The berries are a key flavouring of gin.

CULTIVATION

- From seeds taken from ripe berries during autumn and over winter.

- Plant out after one to two years. They are very slow-growing and benefit from a little care.

- From cuttings of first year's growth in spring or autumn.

WARNING

Berries should not be taken during pregnancy or for kidney disease. The oil should only be prescribed for internal use by professionals.

- Male and female plants are required for berry production, but only female plants produce berries. Male flowers are less numerous and grow in yellow cones. Female flowers grow in green cones.

- Trim juniper to shape by cutting back old wood, which will not re-grow.
- Harvest the berries in late summer when ripe and allow to dry spread out on a tray.
- Can be grown in a suitable-sized container.

Lady's mantle
Alchemilla mollis

Family: Rosaceae
Description: hardy perennial
Ideal habitat: adaptable to dry, shady and damp temperate regions
Part used: leaf

This plant is native to the mountains of Europe. Its botanical name means 'little magical one', a reference to its ability to collect water in its leaves, particularly early morning dew. Its common name is due to another of its supposed magical powers. The story goes that a young lady must collect the early morning dew that lies in its leaves to preserve her youthful looks. She has to do so in the month of May, alone, naked and barefoot in the full moonlight.

It was also dedicated to the Virgin Mary, and used to regulate menstruation, to ease the effects of the menopause and to reduce inflammation in the female organs. Women would also apply the leaves to their breasts to help recover their shape after childbirth. It is still used in herbal medicine today.

USES

Culinary: the mild, bitter taste of the young leaves can be used in salads.

Medicinal: its alpine cousin is used for menstrual disorders.

Other: green dye can be made from the leaves.

CULTIVATION

- Self-seeds easily.
- By root division in spring or autumn.
- Cut off flower heads to prevent self-seeding.
- Will grow in a container or hanging basket.
- Harvest young leaves after the dew has dried.

Lavender
Lavendula augustifolia

Family: Labiatae/Lamiaceae
Description: hardy
Ideal habitat: sunny, well-drained site,
    temperate regions
Parts used: flower, leaf, oil

The Romans first recognised the herb lavender; it was infused in their bath water and its name is derived from *lava*, meaning 'to wash'. Its fragrance was popular in Tudor times and was found to be helpful in relieving rheumatism. In Victorian times it was often sold on the streets of London. It was used for its insect-repelling properties and for masking unpleasant smells; it was also frequently carried around to deflect pestilence and disease.

Native to the Mediterranean and other hot climates, it is now grown extensively in France and in Norfolk, England for the perfume industry. There are very many species of lavender, even white lavenders, all of which have delightful aromas.

USES

Culinary: used in Provençal cooking, and can make pleasant biscuits and sorbets.

Medicinal: has a strong bacterial action which helps heal cuts. Also used for stings and burns.

Other: used extensively in the perfume industry and for potpourri. Used in aromatherapy as a massage oil, for burning and adding to bath water.

CULTIVATION

- From seed sown in spring or autumn.
- From softwood cuttings in spring.
- From hardwood cuttings in summer or early autumn.
- Allow roots to develop over winter before planting out the following year.
- Layering in autumn.
- Clip in early spring and cut back in early autumn, but only the new year's growth.
- Replace the plant if it looks very old and misshapen.
- Can be grown successfully in a suitable-sized container.
- Pick flowers as they open for drying.

Lemon balm
Melissa officinalis

Family: Labiatae/Laminaceae
Alternative name: melissa
Description: hardy perennial
Ideal habitat: sun or partial
    shade, moist, temperate
    regions
Parts used: whole plant, leaf, oil

The Ancient Greeks used lemon balm over 2,000 years ago and it was they who gave it the name *melissa* from the Greek word for 'bee'; it was thought that placing lemon balm in an empty hive would induce bees to enter. The high price of both honey and sugar meant that this tradition was carried on into the Middle Ages.

Although native to the Mediterranean, lemon balm grows throughout North America and in Britain. The herb yields a volatile lemon-scented oil, which has antiviral properties. Drinking lemon balm tea was said to promote long life. However, it was more often used for relieving melancholy.

USES

Culinary: leaves used in salads, sauces and herb
vinegars.

Medicinal: internally for digestive disorders when
linked to nervous tension. Externally for herpes,
sores, gout and insect bites.

Other: used in aromatherapy to relax and rejuvenate.
An ingredient in the liqueurs Benedictine and
Chartreuse. Also good as an insect repellent.

CULTIVATION

- From seed in spring.
- From softwood cuttings in late spring or early
  summer.
- By division of roots in spring or autumn.
- Cut back after flowering to produce new foliage.
- Can be grown as a container plant.
- Pick leaves throughout summer for fresh use.
- For drying, pick just before flowering.
- Handle gently to avoid bruising.
- Drying and storing reduces aroma and therapeutic
  value.

Lemon grass
Cymbopogon citratus

Family: Graminae
Alternative names: sera, takrai, zabalin
Description: tender perennial
Ideal habitat: tropical and subtropical
  regions
Part used: leaf base

Lemon grass only yields
its aroma when it is cut,
imparting the lemon flavour. Lemon rind is often used
as an alternative in cooking on occasions when lemon
grass is not available.

Although it is grown mainly in Southeast Asia, India
and other tropical countries, it is possible to grow it as
an ornamental houseplant in other more temperate
climates, provided its surroundings are kept at a
suitable temperature.

USES

Culinary: mainly used in stir-fry dishes, but also used in soups, curries and pickles, it goes well with coconut milk.

Medicinal: the oil has been used in ointments for the treatment of rheumatic conditions and for sprains. Also used for athlete's foot and the treatment of lice.

Other: used in perfumes and in aromatherapy where its antiseptic properties are said to be excellent for aching feet.

CULTIVATION

- Propagate by division in spring.
- Requires well-drained soil and a minimum temperature of 7 °C (45 °F).
- Stems are cut at ground level for use fresh or dried.
- Not normally grown in temperate regions, but can be grown in a container. Seeds are now available from commercial seed growers.
- Crop as required.

Lemon verbena
Aloysia triphylla

Family: Verbenaceae
Description: half-hardy, deciduous
Ideal habitat: sunny, humid climate in
  well-drained, temperate
  regions
Parts used: leaf, oil

Lemon verbena was once a very
popular plant, yielding a delightful fragrance
that lingers. However, this native Chilean plant was
expensive as a perfume ingredient and its popularity
waned when it was found to sensitise the skin to
sunlight. The more amenable **lemon grass** is used as an
alternative.

USES

Culinary: used in herb teas and to flavour stuffings and salads. Can also be added to ice creams for extra flavour.

Medicinal: tea if taken at bedtime promotes sleep. The oil is both insecticidal and bactericidal.

Other: the leaves make an excellent addition to potpourri and are used in the perfume industry.

CULTIVATION

- From seed, which only grows in warm climates, but can be grown in a heated propagator.
- From softwood cuttings in spring, but they tend to wilt quickly.
- From semi-hardwood cuttings taken in summer or autumn.
- Trim established plants in spring, cut back in autumn and protect in winter.
- New growth may take some time to come through so do not discard the plant if it fails to grow.
- Can be grown in a container and moved into a greenhouse or conservatory.
- Leaves can be picked at any time.

Liquorice
Glycyrrhiza glabra

Family: Leguminosae/Papilonaceae
Alternative name: sweetwood
Description: hardy perennial
Ideal habitat: rich
  Mediterranean soils
Part used: root

Although native to the Mediterranean, liquorice is grown commercially in Iran, India and Russia. It has a liking for long hot summers, and for this reason it is surprising that it thrived in Yorkshire, where it was grown in Pontefract Castle.

The first recorded use of liquorice was by the Egyptians 3,000 years ago. The name combines *glykys*, derived from the Latin for 'sweet', and *rhiza*, meaning 'root'. The plant was brought to England in the 16th century and became a very important crop, although it is not grown here commercially now.

USES

Medicinal: the liquorice juice from the roots is used to mask unpleasant flavours of other medicines, but its most important use is as a laxative. It is also useful in relieving heartburn and stomach ulcers.

Other: used as a flavouring for Guinness and other beers and soft drinks. Also used as a foaming agent for fire extinguishers.

CULTIVATION

- Seeds can be very difficult to germinate in cooler climates.
- By root division in spring or autumn in a rich, deep, well-drained soil.
- Protect plants in first year in cold climates.
- Use roots when three to four years old.
- Best grown in Mediterranean-type conditions.
- Water well in free-draining areas.

WARNING

Excessive doses of liquorice may cause headaches, high blood pressure and water retention.

Lovage
Levisticum officinale

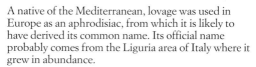

Family: Umbelliferae/Apiaceae
Alternative name: love parsley,
   sea parsley, smallage
Description: hardy perennial
Ideal habitat: prefers sunny,
   well-drained, temperate
   regions
Parts used: leaf, stem, root, seed, oil

A native of the Mediterranean, lovage was used in Europe as an aphrodisiac, from which it is likely to have derived its common name. Its official name probably comes from the Liguria area of Italy where it grew in abundance.

The leaves of lovage, which are similar to celery, have a deodorising and antiseptic effect that led to them being used during the Middle Ages to cover the shoes of tired travellers at the end of the day. The seeds were originally used by the Ancient Greeks, who would chew them to help with digestion and to relieve flatulence.

USES

Culinary: young shoots can be cooked and eaten as a vegetable, the stalks candied like **angelica**, and the seeds used in bread, cheese and biscuits.

Medicinal: internally for indigestion, wind and colic, externally for sores and ulcers.

Other: used in commercial food flavouring and in alcoholic beverages.

CULTIVATION

- From seed in spring.
- By root division in spring or autumn.
- Clip during summer to preserve its shape.
- Prefers rich, well-drained soil.
- The seeds should be harvested as they turn brown.
- The roots can be harvested after two to three years.
- Lovage is a tall plant which needs to be grown in a large container if it is to do well as a potted herb.

Mace

See **Nutmeg**

Makrut lime
Citrus hystrix

Family: Makrut
Alternative name: kaffir lime
Description: tender evergreen tree
Ideal habitat: tropical climates with rich, well-drained soil
Parts used: leaf, rind of fruit

The leaves of the makrut lime are unusual as they grow in pairs in a figure of eight, with a distinctive lemon-lime aroma and flavour. The plant is a very important ingredient in Thai cooking and the full flavour is only realised when the leaves are shredded.

USES

Culinary: leaves are used in soups and curries and also provide a distinctive flavour to fish and chicken dishes. The fruit rind is used in Thai and Indonesian dishes.
Medicinal: the juice of the fruit has been used in Thai creams and shampoos and for tonics in Malaysia.

CULTIVATION

- From seed in spring.
- From semi-ripe cuttings in summer as seeds do not always come true.
- Does not transplant easily.
- Leaves are picked as required.
- Not normally grown in temperate regions but can be grown in a container pot as long as it is kept frost-free.

Mallow
Malva sylvestris

Family: Malvaceae
Description: biennial
Ideal habitat: sun/partial shade,
   well-drained, temperate regions
Parts used: leaf, flower, fruit

Grown since Roman times as a medicinal and pot herb, the word mallow may well have derived from the Greek word meaning 'to soften', since the herb has softening and healing properties.

During Roman times the young shoots were eaten as a vegetable. It was used in the Middle Ages for its calming effect and was thought to be an antidote to aphrodisiacs and love potions.

USES

Culinary: young leaves and shoots can be used in salads or cooked. The unripe seeds can also be used in salads.

Medicinal: externally used to dress skin rashes, eczema, boils, ulcers and insect bites. Can be used internally for coughs, bronchitis and as a mouthwash.

Other: leaves can be used in potpourri.

CULTIVATION

- From seed in autumn, though germination is erratic.
- From softwood cuttings in late spring.
- Trim after flowering.
- Pick young leaves as required during spring.
- For potpourri, pick leaves after flowering.

Marigold, Pot
Calendula officinalis

Family: Compositae
Alternative names: bull's eye, holligold,
    marybud, souci
Description: annual
Ideal habitat: prefers dry,
    temperate regions
Parts used: flower, leaf

Marigold was originally a native of the Mediterranean but is now grown throughout the world. The Egyptians used marigold as a rejuvenating herb, while the Greeks used it to garnish and colour food. During the American Civil War the plant was used to dress open wounds. In India, floral wreaths made of marigolds were used to crown the gods and goddesses.

More romantically, marigolds were also considered an emblem of love and an important potion ingredient by which young maidens would learn of their future love; indeed if you dreamt of marigolds then it was a good sign.

USES

Culinary: a poor man's substitute for **saffron** to colour rice. Also adds colour to other foods such as cheese, butter and soups. The leaves can be used in salads.

Medicinal: the flowers are antiseptic and antifungal, and have been used to help treat stomach ulcers, swollen glands and for menstrual problems. Used externally for skin conditions such as thrush and herpes to help clear the skin.

Other: used as a fabric dye.

CULTIVATION

- From seed in spring or autumn for early flowering, but protect over winter.
- Prefers dry, sunny soil and will tolerate poor conditions.
- Deadhead to prolong flowering.
- Pick flowers just as they open; they can be used fresh or dried.
- Leaves can only be used fresh.

Marjoram

See **Oregano**

Meadowsweet
Filipendula ulmaria

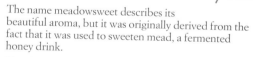

Family: Rosaceae
Alternative names: bridewort, meadow queen
Description: hardy perennial
Ideal habitat: damp meadows or wetlands, temperate regions
Parts used: whole plant, flower

The name meadowsweet describes its beautiful aroma, but it was originally derived from the fact that it was used to sweeten mead, a fermented honey drink.

The druids regarded meadowsweet as sacred. It was also a favourite of Elizabeth I, who adorned her bedchamber with it. Often used as a strewing herb in churches, meadowsweet was also a common bridal flower, and was sometimes known as bridewort.

Meadowsweet is rich in salicylic acid, the active ingredient of aspirin.

> **WARNING**
>
> Not to be used on people who are sensitive to salicylic acid.

USES

Medicinal: a traditional remedy for acidic stomachs, for diarrhoea in children, and for rheumatic complaints, joint pains, flu and cystitis.

Other: flowers can be used in potpourri, while the roots can be used to make a black dye.

CULTIVATION

- From seeds in spring or autumn.
- By root division in autumn.
- Cut back flowers in summer.
- Prefers semi-shaded, moist soils.
- Pick leaves fresh before the herb flowers.
- Pick flowers just as they open; can be dried.
- Can be grown in a container but keep moist and semi-shaded.

Mint
Mentha spp.

Family: Labiatae
Description: hardy perennial
Ideal habitat: very adaptable,
   temperate regions
Parts used: whole plant, leaf, oil

Mints are native to Europe where they were first cultivated for their medicinal properties. The Japanese cultivated mint for its menthol over 2,000 years ago, and it even appeared in Greek mythology when a nymph was turned into the beautifully scented mint plant following jealous rivalry between the queen and the nymph Minthe. In more recent times the settlers took mint to the New World where they grew it in their gardens for both culinary and medicinal purposes.

There is an enormous variety of mints, all of which contain the characteristic volatile oil,

WARNING

Pennyroyal should not be used during pregnancy or if you suffer from kidney disease.

menthol, which gives mint its smell and taste. However, there are subtle differences between each of the mints. The most familiar are pennyroyal (*Mentha pulegium*), apple mint (*Mentha gentilis*), pineapple mint (*Mentha suaveolens*), spearmint (*Mentha spicata*) and peppermint (*Mentha piperita*).

USES

Culinary: mint is a traditional British accompaniment to lamb, and is also added to peas and potatoes. Pennyroyal is a common addition to black puddings and to Spanish sausages. Some mints are attractive garnishes. Spearmint also contains carvone, a volatile oil also found in **caraway**.

Medicinal: peppermint tea is used to help indigestion.

Other: used in oral hygiene preparations, as food flavourings, and in the liqueur crème de menthe. Peppermint is used in aromatherapy as a massage oil and is also added to bath water to ease muscle fatigue. Pennyroyal contains pulegone, which is also found in **calamint**, and is a good insect repellent.

CULTIVATION

- Pennyroyal is most successful if grown from seed.

- Root division is most successful for all mints.

- Mint can be very invasive, so it is best to grow it in a container.

> ### WARNING
> The oil from mint may cause an allergic reaction. Prolonged inhalation should be avoided. Do not use the herb on babies.

- Dry sunny or shaded positions with poor soil are best for mints, the exception being pennyroyal, which particularly likes a rich, well-drained soil but does not thrive in wet winters, so it is best moved to a greenhouse or conservatory.

- Pick leaves fresh throughout the season.

- Pick leaves for drying or freezing before flowering.

- Do not grow different species of mint together since they are prone to lose their individual scent under these circumstances.

Mustard seed
Brassica alba (white)
Brassica juncea (brown)
Brassica nigra (black)

Family: Cruciferae
Description: hardy
Ideal habitat: adaptable – white is
   traditionally a Mediterranean
   crop, while brown is usually found in India
Parts used: leaf, seed

Mustard is mentioned many times in the history
books, but particularly in the Bible where the
kingdom of heaven is likened to a grain of mustard
seed. The seed, though small, yields a very large plant.
It is reported that Darius III of Persia sent Alexander
the Great a bag of sesame seeds to indicate the
numbers in his army. Alexander returned this gesture
with a bag of mustard seeds to symbolise not only
numbers but strength.

It is thought that the name 'mustard' is derived from
the Latin word *must*, which was the name of the grape

juice used to mix the mustard powder to a paste. Mustard powder should be mixed with cold water and made 10 minutes before it is used, as an enzyme is activated which helps bring about the best flavour. Adding vinegar or hot water deactivates the enzyme and a bitter flavour is produced.

WARNING

Prolonged skin contact may be harmful, especially if the skin is sensitive.

White mustard is native to the Mediterranean and is also used in the USA. The French tend to use black or brown mustard, although black is starting to predominate because it is more easily harvested. The British use a mixture of white and black mustard.

USES

Culinary: young leaves can be cooked as a vegetable, while the seeds can be ground to a paste to make mustard or added to pickles and curries.

Medicinal: used externally as a poultice. A mustard footbath is the traditional remedy for colds and headaches; skin contact causes increased blood flow and helps the removal of toxins.

Brown mustard seeds
(brassica juncea)

CULTIVATION

- Normally grown as a crop product from seed sown in spring.
- Requires rich, well-drained soil.
- Leaves and flowers should be picked when young.
- Pick pods as they begin to ripen, then dry.
- Seed keeps very well.

Nasturtium
Tropaeolum majus

Family: Tropaeolaceae
Alternative names: Indian cress, large cress
Description: half-hardy annual
Ideal habitat: sunny, well-drained temperate regions
Parts used: leaf, flower, seed

The nasturtium family is native to South America but is now cultivated everywhere. The name is probably derived from the Latin word for 'trophy', because historically, following a battle, a tree trunk would be dressed with helmets and shields. The huge green leaves of the plant have been thought to resemble shields, and the vibrant orange/red flowers have been likened to bloodstained helmets.

The sulphur-rich herb had a reputation for retarding baldness, while the leaves are rich in vitamin C and so helped to cure scurvy. Most nasturtiums are now grown for their appearance, not their culinary or medicinal properties.

USES

Culinary: use leaves in salads. Flowers can be used too since they have a peppery flavour. The seeds can be pickled as a substitute for capers.

Medicinal: good for poor skin (it has antiseptic properties), and also for respiratory infections.

Other: used in hair lotion.

CULTIVATION

- From seeds in spring.
- Do not feed as the plant then produces more leaves at the expense of flowers.
- Prefers poor soil in full sun or partial shade.
- Sensitive to frost.
- Flowers can only be used fresh.
- Pick seed leaves for fresh use as required.
- Pick seed pods before they lose their green colour for pickling in vinegar as poor man's capers.

WARNING

Avoid eating more than 15 g of nasturtium on any one occasion and 25 g per day.

Nettle
Urtica dioica

Family: Urticaceae
Description: hardy perennial
Ideal habitat: temperate regions,
   though very tolerant of all
   conditions
Parts used: whole plant,
   leaf

Nettle is an ancient herb. Nettle cloth has been found from the Bronze Age. Roman soldiers would flog themselves with the plants to stimulate circulation, and the burning sensation that they felt on contact with the nettle would keep them warm.

Before World War II, nettles were imported to Britain from Germany and processed into the dye from which camouflage was made.

Nutritionally, the nettle is rich in vitamins A and C, and iron, and also contains histamine and serotonin.

USES

Culinary: young leaves are cooked as a vegetable with a similar flavour to spinach; raw leaves should be avoided. Nettle soup is sometimes made and nettle wine used to be popular.

Medicinal: helps with anaemia and haemorrhage.

Other: used for their high chlorophyll content, responsible for the additive E140.

CULTIVATION

- From seed in spring.
- By root division of established plants.
- Cut back if invasive.
- Has few problems with pests. Attracts butterflies.
- Prefers damp, rich soils.
- Pick young leaves in spring for use as a vegetable and wear gloves.

WARNING

Old nettle leaves develop oxalate crystals which can cause kidney stones. It is best to use only young leaves when cooking.

Nigella
Nigella sativa

Family: Ranunculaceae
Alternative name: kalonji
Description: hardy annual
Ideal habitat: sunny, well-drained, temperate regions
Parts used: seed, oil

Nigella originates from India where most of it now grows. It is closely related to the common English flower 'love in the mist' (*Nigella damascena*) which grows very easily in many gardens. The tiny black seeds have very little flavour until they are rubbed, when they release a peppery smell. Nigella seeds have also been used as a substitute for pepper. Used in Islamic medicine, they were also exported to Malaysia for medicinal purposes but their use dates back to Roman times.

USES

Culinary: one of the five spices in the Bengali five-spice mix. Found widely in Indian cooking, the seeds are often used in naan bread. Can also be mixed with sesame seeds and used in Middle Eastern breads.

Medicinal: a remedy for painful menstruation as well as post-childbirth contractions and poor lactation.

Other: *Nigella damascena* seeds are distilled for use in lipsticks and perfumes.

CULTIVATION

- Grows easily from seed in autumn in well-drained soil on a sunny site.
- Seeds harvested on ripening.
- *Nigella sativa* is not normally grown in the UK, although the English cousin, love in the mist, is a common plant.

Nigella (nigella damascena)

Nutmeg
Myristica fragrans

Family: Myristicaceae
Description: evergreen tree
Ideal habitat: tropical climates
Parts used: nut – nutmeg; outer casing – mace

Nutmeg and mace are different parts of the nutmeg fruit. Mace is the outer covering of the nut; nutmeg is the kernel.

WARNING
Use sparingly; can cause hallucination or even death.

Nutmeg has been used since Roman times, and one Roman emperor even had the streets fumigated with nutmegs prior to his coronation.

The nutmeg tree was a valuable crop to the Dutch who fought hard to restrict its availability in order to keep its price high and to restrict its growth to only two islands. The Dutch were thwarted by fruit pigeons that carried the seeds from the closely guarded Spice Islands to other nearby islands, thus giving others the opportunity to profit from the spice.

USES

Culinary: mace is usually used in savoury dishes, while nutmeg mainly appears in sweet dishes, such as rice pudding and egg custard.

Medicinal: nutmeg is a narcotic, though not of value in the amounts used in cooking. It is also an astringent and stimulant, and possesses aphrodisiac properties.

Other: used in perfumes. Mace is used in sprays as a deterrent against attackers, although it is not legal in the UK.

CULTIVATION

- From seed in spring.
- Produces nutmegs after 15–20 years.
- Will crop for 30–40 years subsequently.
- The fruit when ripe splits to reveal the mace (bright red arils) encasing the nut.
- The mace is removed from the kernel (nutmeg) and dried.
- Damaged kernels are discarded.
- Not normally grown in temperate climates.

Oregano
Origanum vulgare
(Wild marjoram/Oregano)
Origanum majorana
(Sweet marjoram/Knotted marjoram)

Family: Labiateae/Lamiaceae
Alternative names: marjolaine,
  mountain mint, origan, winter
  sweet
Description: hardy perennial
  (*Origanum vulgare*); annual
  (*Origanum majorana*)
Ideal habitat: dry, sunny, well-drained,
  temperate regions
Part used: leaf

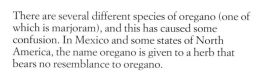

There are several different species of oregano (one of
which is marjoram), and this has caused some
confusion. In Mexico and some states of North
America, the name oregano is given to a herb that
bears no resemblance to oregano.

The name oregano is derived from the Greek *oros* ('mountain') and *ganos* ('joy'), since this herb is commonly found on the dry mountainous Mediterranean slopes. Both the Ancient Greeks and Romans used it in their baths and as massage oil, and as a disinfectant and preservative. It was also used in nosegays to help deter the plague and pestilence.

USES

Culinary: used in Italian, Greek and Mexican cooking, usually combined with strongly flavoured foods.

Medicinal: as medicine for colds, bronchitis, asthma, flu and minor fevers. Applied externally for strains, arthritis and muscular pain, and also to kill lice. Contains thymol.

Other: used in aromatherapy to help reduce anxiety, and commercially for food flavourings and perfumes.

CULTIVATION

- From seed in spring when germination can be erratic.
- From root division during winter.
- Cut flowers after flowering to maintain shape.
- In autumn cut back the growth.

- Sweet marjoram is best treated as an annual and sown every year. However, in Mediterranean climates it is a half-hardy perennial.
- Pick leaves as required.
- Can be grown in containers, but protect the more tender varieties in winter.

Papaya seeds
Carica papaya

Family: Caricaceae
Description: herbaceous perennial
Ideal habitat: tropical climates
Parts used: seed, sap

The fast-growing papaya tree produces fruit that can weigh up to 9 kg (20 lb). The seeds are enclosed in the berries. The slightly aromatic seeds tend to lose their aroma as they dry, but have a taste that resembles **mustard** and cress. Australian Aborigines thought the seeds were of value as an aphrodisiac.

The papaya tree can be tapped for sap in a similar manner to the rubber tree. The sap and the seeds both contain a proteolytic enzyme, papain, which breaks down proteins and is used as a meat tenderiser.

USES

Culinary: tough meat is made tender when rubbed with the crushed seeds or sap. The seeds can be added to fruit salads as well as salad dressings.

Medicinal: in India the seeds are used as a breath freshener, but were also widely used as pessaries for flatulence and piles.

Other: papain from the seeds and sap is used commercially as a meat tenderiser.

CULTIVATION

- From seed in spring.
- Requires a rich, moist soil.
- Grown in the tropics at low altitudes.
- Seed harvested from ripe fruit.
- Papain extracted from unripe fruit and sap.
- Not normally grown in the UK.

Paprika

See **Chilli**

Parsley
Petroselinum crispum

Family: Umbelliferae/Apiaceae
Description: hardy biennial
Ideal habitat: warm, rich,
    well-drained, temperate
    regions
Parts used: leaf, root, seed, oil

Parsley is the best-known herb
used for garnishing foods, but
it was not always popular as an
edible herb. It was originally
used to decorate crowns in
Ancient Greek times. It was
the Romans who started to eat
parsley, their belief being that it
would help avoid the perils of
drink and overcome unpleasant odours.

WARNING

Avoid medicinally
during pregnancy.
The oil should
only be used
under medical
supervision.

The herb is not the easiest to grow from seed, and as a result it has been said that only witches and pregnant women could make it grow. It is worthwhile making the effort since it is such a good source of vitamins C and A, and it makes a useful contribution to iron intake.

USES

Culinary: enhances the flavour of bland foods, and is used in stuffings, sauces and fish dishes. It is an ingredient of fines herbes, and is often used in bouquet garni.

Medicinal: useful for treating urinary infections, and also used for post-partum contractions.

Other: used in commercial food flavourings and male perfumes. An infusion of crushed seeds will kill head lice.

CULTIVATION

- From seed in spring or autumn.
- Requires a rich, well-drained soil.
- Cut flower heads in summer.
- Pick leaves as required.
- Protect in colder months for continuous picking.

Passionflower
Passiflora incarnata

Family: Passifloraceae
Alternative name: maypops
Description: hardy
Ideal habitat: sunny,
   slightly acid, well-
   drained soil,
   temperate regions
Parts used: whole plant, root

Historically, the passionflower was a potent symbol for South American missionaries, for whom the stigma and stamens represented the nails and wounds of Christ respectively, with each of the ten petals representing the loyal apostles.

It became a popular treatment for insomnia, although earlier it was used as a treatment for epilepsy. Passionflower contains alkaloids which are effective and non-addictive sedatives which cause drowsiness.

USES

Culinary: the fruit can be used for jam and desserts.

Medicinal: best known for its ability to relieve insomnia alongside **camomile**, **hops** and **valerian**, but also thought to be useful for relieving nervous tension, pre-menstrual tension and for irritable bowel syndrome (IBS). Also useful for hypertension.

CULTIVATION

- From seed in spring but requires warmth: 18–21 °C (64–70 °F).
- From semi-ripe cuttings in summer.
- Germination can be slow.
- Cut back in spring.
- Fruits picked when ripe for culinary purposes.
- Harvest plant for drying for infusions and tinctures.

Pennyroyal

See **Mint**

Pepper
Piper nigrum

Family: Piperaceae
Description: tender perennial
Ideal habitat: hot, frost-
    free climates
Part used: fruit

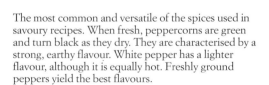

The most common and versatile of the spices used in
savoury recipes. When fresh, peppercorns are green
and turn black as they dry. They are characterised by a
strong, earthy flavour. White pepper has a lighter
flavour, although it is equally hot. Freshly ground
peppers yield the best flavours.

USES

Culinary: used in most savoury dishes. Crushed
   peppercorns are often used on steaks and oily fish.
Medicinal: used for indigestion and wind, and in
   China for stomach chills and food poisoning. Used
   in Ayurvedic medicine as an anti-emetic.
Other: in East Africa it is thought that eating large
   quantities of pepper produces a body odour that
   repels mosquitoes.

CULTIVATION

- From semi-ripe cuttings in summer; requires rich,
  deep soil, but will tolerate clay.
- Grown as a vine against frames; cut back young
  plants to stimulate growth.
- Requires three to five years to bear the flowers from
  which fruit develop.
- Vines may be viable for up to 40 years.
- Fruits picked unripe and used fresh as pickled
  peppercorns or dried as black peppercorns.
- White peppercorns are produced by soaking
  peppercorns under slowly running water so that the
  outer husk rots and can be easily removed.

Peppermint

See **Mint**

Pomegranate
Punica granatum

Family: Punicaceae
Description: tender half-hardy
Ideal habitat: adaptable
Parts used: root, bark, seed, oil

Once thought of as the apple in the Garden of Eden, pomegranate was frequently mentioned in the Bible. Young brides in Turkey predicted the number of children they would have by dropping a pomegranate onto the ground. For each seed that spilled, they believed a child would be born to them.

Pomegranate seeds have a bittersweet flavour with an astringent smell; the juice has a sweet smell; the syrup flavour is intense. Seeds can be dried for domestic use.

USES

Culinary: dried, crushed seeds are used for
garnishes. Very popular in Middle Eastern
cooking, but in India their purpose is to make
foods more sour. Used to make grenadine.

Medicinal: used for chronic dysentery and diarrhoea
as it helps destroy parasites and has some antiviral control. Also used externally for cold sores
and throat infections.

Other: an ingredient in a daiquiri cocktail.

CULTIVATION

- From seed in spring in a well-drained, sunny
  position (22 °C/72 °F).
- From semi-ripe cuttings in summer.
- From root cuttings in autumn.
- To fruit, long, hot summers with cooler winters are
  required.
- Will tolerate freezing temperatures but only for a
  short time.

Poppy
Papaver rhoeas
(corn poppy)
Papaver somniferum
(opium poppy)

Family: Papaveraceae
Description: hardy annual
Ideal habitat: well-drained,
  sunny, temperate regions
Parts used: flower, seed

Traditionally, poppies were seen in
cornfields. However, recent intensive farming has seen
their demise. They have since become better known as
the symbol of Remembrance Day, following the death
of so many soldiers in Flanders where poppies grew
prolifically. The Romans regarded the corn poppy as
sacred. It contains some alkaloids but is more
important for its red pigment.

The opium poppy, however, contains more powerful
alkaloids, in particular morphine and codeine.

Field poppy (papaver rhoeas)

Morphine is a very potent, addictive painkiller, and is therefore very carefully controlled and subject to legal restrictions in many countries.

USES

Culinary: the seeds of both plants are free of alkaloids and can be used in cookery, often sprinkled on breads or biscuits and as a garnish.

Medicinal: both types of poppy seed are used in Ayurvedic medicine for digestive complaints. The opium poppy is used commercially for pain relief.

Other: the red flower petals of the corn poppy are used for colouring medicines and wine and are also added to potpourri.

CULTIVATION

- From seed in spring or autumn in a well-drained, sunny site (self-seed easily).
- Does not transplant well.
- Harvest seeds from ripe pods.
- The latex (raw opium) is extracted from the green part of the flower once the petals are shed.

WARNING

All parts of the poppy, except for the seed, are toxic if eaten.

Red clover
Trifolium pratense

Family: Leguminosae/Papilionaceae
Description: hardy perennial
Ideal habitat: temperate regions
Part used: flowering top

Clover has become important in organic agriculture as part of the crop rotation system, due to its ability to encourage nitrogen retention in the soil.

WARNING
Avoid during pregnancy and breast-feeding.

Between 1941 and 1944 a New Zealand farmer noticed that the fertility of his sheep was reduced, despite the fact that they looked healthy. The sheep had been feeding on red clover. Analysis of the clover revealed that it was high in isoflavones, and in particular genistein (also found in soya), which has oestrogen-like properties. The farmer found that taking the sheep away from the field of red clover restored their fertility.

USES

Medicinal: most important for its ability to relieve the symptoms of menopause and therefore reduce the likelihood of heart disease in post-menopausal women, it is also thought to be anti-inflammatory and helpful as part of cancer treatment.

CULTIVATION

- From seed in spring.
- By division of plants in spring.
- Prefers a moist, drained, sunny site with neutral soil.
- Harvest flower heads as they open.

Rocket, Salad
Eruca vesicaria subsp. sativa

Family: Cruciferae/Brassicaceae
Alternative names: arugula, rucola
Description: half-hardy annual
Ideal habitat: temperate regions
Part used: leaf

Now a popular salad herb, salad rocket originally had medicinal uses. It was a native of the Mediterranean and later brought to the shores of the UK, where the Elizabethans became very partial to it.

Historically, it has been reported that salad rocket should be eaten by a person who is to be whipped, as it is supposed to alleviate the pain of the event. It was also reported as a protection against the bites of tiny mammals and venomous creatures.

USES

Culinary: most commonly used as a salad leaf, the young leaves are the most tender and least bitter.
Medicinal: originally used in cough medicine.

CULTIVATION

- Treat as an annual; sow from seed in spring in rich, moist soil in a shady area.
- Continuously harvest leaves to prevent flowering.
- Avoid using fertiliser as this produces plenty of leaves but with little flavour.

Rocket, Sweet
Hesperis matronalis

Family: Cruciferae
Alternative names: damask violet and dame's violet
Description: hardy biennial
Ideal habitat: temperate climates
Parts used: leaf, flower

The delightful aroma of sweet rocket is at its best in the evening. Its use dates back to Ancient Greek times, where it derived its name from the Greek *hesperos*, which means 'evening'. Its native home is Italy, but it grows freely elsewhere.

USES

Culinary: if picked young, the leaves can be used in salads, but are slightly bitter.
Other: the dried flowers can be used in potpourri for both their colour and their scent.

CULTIVATION

- From seed in the spring or autumn; if sown in spring they may flower during their first year.
- Requires well-drained, fertile soil.
- May send out shoots from its original roots and therefore behave as a perennial.
- Pick leaves when young.
- Pick flowers as they open.

Rosemary
Rosmarinus officinalis

Family: Labiatae/Laminaceae
Description: evergreen hardy perennial
Ideal habitat: well-drained, sunny, sheltered position, temperate regions
Parts used: leaf, flower, oil

Rosemary was carried by both mourners and brides and is a symbol of friendship and loyalty. It was also used, as was **thyme**, to purify the air for the sick and to help ward off 'jail fever'. Rosemary has a long history, dating back to ancient times, where its name in Latin meant 'sea dew'. This name reflected its tendency to grow close to the sea.

The volatile oils known as flavanols, and phenolic acids found in rosemary are antiseptic and anti-inflammatory. Toxic shock syndrome has been treated with rosmarinic acid. Diosmin, a volatile oil found in rosemary, is said to be more potent than rutin (found in **rue**) for maintaining capillary wall strength.

USES

Culinary: associated with lamb dishes. Used to flavour oils, vinegars and dressings. Releases a delicious aroma if burnt on a barbecue when cooking.

Medicinal: used externally for rheumatism, arthritis and muscular pains. Used internally for migraine, nervous exhaustion and anxiety.

Other: used in skin, hair and bath preparations. Also used in aromatherapy as a massage oil, for burning, and adding to bath water, to promote mental stimulation and help muscular fatigue.

CULTIVATION

- Can be grown from seed in spring.
- Most reliably grown from softwood cuttings in spring.
- May also be grown from semi-hardwood cuttings in summer.
- Rosemary plant can also be layered.
- Trim after flowering.
- Protect young plants in winter.
- Old bushes should be replaced every five to six years.
- Leaves and flowers should be picked in spring and early summer.

WARNING

- Oil should not be used internally.
- Large doses of the plant's leaf are toxic, and may cause poisoning and abortion, and more rarely death.

Rue
Ruta graveolens

Family: Rutaceae
Alternative names: herbygrass, herb of grace
Description: hardy evergreen perennial
Ideal habitat: poor-quality soil, Mediterranean climates
Part used: leaf

Rue has adapted itself to cooler climates. It has a bitter taste and a reputation for providing protection against witchcraft. Rue may be used as an antidote to poisonous toadstools and venomous snakebites. Its powers were also used to protect a judge when prisoners from disease-ridden jails were brought before him.

WARNING

Plant towards the back of the border to avoid too much contact with the plant as it can cause a type of dermatitis. Only take cuttings when the sun is down – sunny or rainy conditions make the plant more dangerous.

A flavanoid, rutin, found in rue, helps protect capillaries from breaking down. This might explain the traditional role of rue in treating poor eyesight. It has been suggested that Leonardo da Vinci and Michelangelo both benefited from the herb.

USES

Culinary: due to its bitter taste it is rarely used in food.
Medicinal: applied externally to help prevent sore eyes, earache and skin diseases, and internally for menstrual problems, colic and epilepsy.
Other: used to flavour the Italian grape spirit known as grappa.

CULTIVATION

- From seed in spring; prefers poor, well-drained soil.
- From softwood cuttings in summer.
- Protect from cold in extreme conditions.
- Leaves are picked in spring and summer.

WARNING

When used for medicinal purposes, should be administered by medical personnel only.

Saffron
Crocus sativus

Family: Iridaceae
Description: hardy bulb
Ideal habitat: warm, sunny,
well-drained soils
Part used: flower stigma

It takes 400 hours picking from 150,000 flowers to produce 1 kg (2.2 lb) of dried saffron. This, the most expensive spice of all, takes its name from the Arabic for 'yellow' and is highly prized for its colour as well as its distinctive lingering warm aroma.

The high cost of saffron has led to a great deal of adulteration, and with it severe penalties on being discovered. Cheaper alternatives such as **turmeric** and safflower have been used, but in terms of quality they do not compare to saffron.

USES

Culinary: used in celebration cooking such as Indian pilau rice, Spanish paella and Italian risotto.

Medicinal: used in Chinese medicine for depression and menstrual disorders.

Other: an ingredient of Chartreuse and also used in perfumes. In common with other foods that are rare and hence seen as possessing special qualities, saffron is believed by some to be an aphrodisiac.

CULTIVATION

- Propagate from offsets of the bulb in late spring.
- Requires a good summer, such as that found in the Mediterranean regions, to thrive.
- Flowers picked when open.
- The dried powder does not keep, so should be used within a year of harvest.

Sage
Salvia spp.

Family: Labiatae/Lamiaceae
Description: annuals, biennials, perennials
Ideal habitat: Mediterranean climates
Parts used: leaf, oil

There is a large number of different species within the sage family. The most common sage (*Salvia officinalis*) is a hardy perennial, whereas the more delicate pineapple sage is a tender perennial from the cooler regions of Europe. The different sages have various culinary, medicinal and aromatic properties for which they have been valued throughout history.

The family name is derived from the Latin word for 'to heal'. Interestingly, recent work has suggested that sage may have properties that help prevent the effects of ageing. It may be that its common name was the result of its ability to ward off disease in the elderly.

USES

Culinary: common sage is used as a flavouring in tea and in the cheese Sage Derby, as well as in stuffings. Pineapple sage is used for pork dishes. It is even used to add flavour to sponge cakes.

Medicinal: used internally for indigestion and wind, and in cases of excess salivation (Parkinson's) and excess perspiration (tuberculosis). Can be used as a gargle for sore throats. Also benefits sore gums and mouth ulcers.

Other: used in perfumes, toiletries and toothpaste.

CULTIVATION

- Common sage is easily grown from seed.
- From softwood cuttings in late spring or winter.
- By layering of established branches.
- Prune plants in spring to protect shape.
- Tender varieties should be overwintered in a conservatory.
- Pick leaves as required; does not dry easily so best to use as a fresh herb.

WARNING

Excessive use of sage is not recommended as its antiseptic properties are potentially toxic.

Sage, Jerusalem
Phlomis fruticosa

Family: Labiatae
Description: hardy evergreen
   perennial
Ideal habitat: sunny, dry,
   well-drained soil, temperate regions
Part used: leaf

Jerusalem sage was originally grown in the
Mediterranean. It is also mentioned in early Greek
medical writings. It is now found throughout Europe
and used for its slightly furry grey aromatic leaves.

USES

Culinary: not commonly used in cooking but can be
   used in stews and casseroles. Popular in Greece.
Other: used in potpourri.

CULTIVATION

• From seeds in autumn, overwintered in a cold frame
  or greenhouse.

- Most reliably from softwood cuttings in summer.
- By root division in spring.
- Protect plants at temperatures below –5 °C (23 °F).
- Is a good container plant in a large pot.
- Trim back after flowering.
- Do not over-water as it is drought-tolerant.

St John's wort
Hypericum perforatum

Family: Guttiferae
Alternative names: warrior's
    wound, amber, touch and heal,
    herb of St John, grace of God
Description: hardy perennial
Ideal habitat: slightly dry,
    temperate regions
Part used: whole plant

Treading on St John's wort after sunset will cause you
to be whisked off on a magic horse and taken round

the heavens, before arriving back exhausted at sunrise – or so it is said. Back on Earth, the herb is relied on by many to lift depression. This is because it contains the active ingredient hypericin.

WARNING

St John's wort may make the skin sensitive to light.

USES

Medicinal: used to treat anxiety, depression, nervous tension, bed wetting and menopausal symptoms.
Other: yellow dye can be extracted from the flowers.

CULTIVATION

- From seed in spring or autumn, tolerates most soils.
- By division in autumn.
- Can be invasive in drier soils.
- Plants can be harvested as flowering begins.
- In Australia subject to statutory control as a weed.

WARNING

Check with your doctor before taking St John's wort as it can affect prescription drugs.

Savory
Satureja hortensis (summer savory)
Satureja montana (winter savory)

Family: Labiatae/Lamiceae
Alternative name: bean herb
Description: half-hardy annual (*Satureja hortensis*); semi-evergreen hardy perennial (*Satureja montana*)
Ideal habitat: sunny, well-drained, temperate regions
Part used: leaf

Winter and summer savory are the most common varieties. Both are rich in volatile oils, especially thymol, though the amounts vary between the species. They have similar aromas to both **thyme** and **marjoram**.

The Ancient Egyptians used savory in their love potions. Although primarily used by the Romans as a food ingredient, it was used as a strewing herb due to its valuable disinfecting properties. Savory is now mainly used as a food ingredient. Both winter and summer savory are said to improve digestion and increase perspiration.

USES

Culinary: summer savory is particularly good with beans (it is known as the bean herb), as it is thought to prevent flatulence. Both are used for savoury dishes and as ingredients in *herbes de Provence*.

Medicinal: used for indigestion, nausea and colic. Summer savory can also be rubbed onto bee stings for pain relief.

Other: used in liqueurs.

CULTIVATION

- From seed in spring.
- Pick summer savory frequently to prevent flowering and to maintain its flavour.
- Protect summer savory from frost.
- Trim winter savory to maintain its shape; makes a good edging plant.

Savory (satureja)

Sesame
Sesamum indicum

Family: Pedaliaceae
Description: half-hardy
Ideal habitat: tropical
   climates
Parts used: leaf, seed, oil

Sesame has been cultivated for thousands of years, and its importance was referred to 5,000 years ago. The Ancient Greeks sprinkled the seeds on bread before baking, a practice which still goes on today. Although originally from Africa, sesame is found in other similar climates, where it is largely grown for local use.

The outer husk of the seeds is either red, yellow, brown or black; when the husk is removed it yields the familiar creamy-coloured seeds. These seeds are good sources of the vitamins A, B and E, as well as calcium. The oil is high in unsaturated oils, which makes sesame a highly nutritious addition to the diet.

USES

Culinary: the seeds are sprinkled over vegetables and salads. Ground with honey sesame makes halva, while as a paste it is known as tahini. It is also added to hummus and other sauces and dips.

Medicinal: has been taken internally for premature hair loss and greying. It helps prevent constipation as well as dental decay and osteoporosis. The oil has been applied externally to help haemorrhoids.

Other: used in the manufacture of soaps and pharmaceuticals, the residue is also fed to livestock.

CULTIVATION

- From seed in spring or autumn in a sunny, well-drained, sandy soil.
- The leaves are picked at any time for infusions.
- The seeds are harvested when ready.
- Not normally grown in temperate climates.

Sorrel
Rumex acetosa

Family: Polygonaceae
Alternative names: thousand fingers, bread and cheese, sour leaves, Tom Thumb
Description: hardy perennial
Ideal habitat: moist, rich acid soil, temperate regions
Part used: leaf

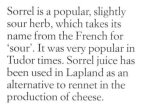

Sorrel is a popular, slightly sour herb, which takes its name from the French for 'sour'. It was very popular in Tudor times. Sorrel juice has been used in Lapland as an alternative to rennet in the production of cheese.

Sorrel is rich in vitamin C, but contains oxalic acid. It is a very close relative of *Rumex crispus*, or the dock leaf.

WARNING

If eaten in large quantities can form stones of calcium oxalate. Not recommended for those with kidney stones, or indeed gout, rheumatism or arthritis.

USES

Culinary: most commonly added to soups and sauces.

Medicinal: rarely used, though a poultice has been used to treat acne.

Other: can be used to make a green dye. The juice also helps to remove mould and rust stains.

CULTIVATION

- From seed in late spring.
- By division in autumn.
- Prefers a damp, rich, acid soil and partial shade.
- Cut flowers to maintain leaf production.
- Pick leaves as required.
- Can be difficult to eradicate. If so, treat with lime as this produces unfavourable conditions for growing.

Spearmint

See **Mint**

Strawberry, Wild
Fragaria vesca

Family: Rosaceae
Description: hardy perennial
Ideal habitat: forests and shady areas, temperate regions
Parts used: leaf, root, fruit

It is often thought that strawberry derived its name from the common practice of placing straw underneath the plant. The real reason, however, is due to the seeds on the outside of the plant, that look like chaff. The wild strawberry has quite small fruit, but there are many cultivated varieties that are grown for the size, shape and the keeping qualities of their fruit.

The fruit is high in vitamin C and has a mildly laxative effect. It is best described as a cooling astringent herb with a slight diuretic effect. The leaves and roots are high in tannins (also found in tea).

USES

Culinary: the leaves may be used to make tea, while the fruit is used to make jams and preserves. It can also be made into drinks, including wine.

Medicinal: the leaves and root, if taken, are said to be good for gout. Externally, the strawberry is good for sunburn, skin blemishes and discoloured teeth.

Other: used in cosmetics, the fruit helps to whiten the skin.

CULTIVATION

- From seed in late autumn.
- Propagate by division of the runners off the mother plant.
- Requires rich soil that does not dry out, in sun or partial shade.
- Does not need winter protection.
- Pick leaves as required and before the fruit sets.
- Pick fruits as they ripen for eating.

WARNING

Some people are allergic to strawberries.

Sweet cicely
Myrrhis odorata

Family: Umbelliferae/Apiaceae
Alternative names: myrrh, roman plant, sweet bracken, sweet fern, switch
Description: hardy perennial
Ideal habitat: light, well-drained soils, temperate climates
Parts used: leaf, root, seed

Sweet cicely contains the same volatile oils found in **fennel**, **anise** and **star anise,** which gives it an aniseed-like flavour, although some describe it as having a parsnip flavour.

Gerard describes the boiled roots of sweet cicely acting as a pick-me-up for 'dull' people, while Culpeper claimed that its roots would help prevent the plague. Sweet cicely is often found in Welsh graveyards, where it is planted to commemorate a loved one. In North America the name sweet cicely has been given to another plant that is not in any way related to this herb.

USES

Culinary: the leaves can be added to stews and
soups, and can also be used as a low-calorie
sweetener. Add to fruits such as rhubarb and
blackcurrants when cooking to reduce tartness.
The seeds can be added to salads.

Medicinal: rarely used, but has been said to be good
for coughs and minor digestive complaints.

Other: appreciated by beekeepers, as it is one of the
first nectar-producing plants.

CULTIVATION

• From seed in autumn.
• From root cuttings in spring and autumn.
• By division of plants.
• Can be invasive in poor, light, well-drained soil – it
  does not like humid conditions.
• Pick young leaves at any time.
• Collect seeds before they ripen and then allow to
  ripen.
• Harvest roots when the plant dies back; can be
  dried or eaten fresh.

Szechuan pepper
Zanthoxylum pipertum

Family: Rutaceae
Description: evergreen hardy tree
Ideal habitat: fertile soils, hot
Parts used: bark, leaf, berry

Szechuan pepper is harvested from the prickly ash tree.
It is closely related to **star anise** rather than **pepper**
from which it derives its name. It is found
predominantly in China's Szechuan region. Unlike with
star anise, the berries are removed as they are bitter.

Its close American cousin, *Zanthoxylum americanum*,
the toothache tree, contains similar alkaloids to
those of the Szechuan pepper and has been used to
treat toothache.

USES

Culinary: used in Chinese food, especially chicken and
duck. Used in Chinese five-spice and Japanese seven-
flavoured seasoning. Leaves are dried and ground to
make sansho, a Japanese spice.
Medicinal: used in digestive complaints.

CULTIVATION

- From seed in autumn.
- From root cuttings in late winter.
- Remove dead wood and cut back in late winter and early spring.
- Enjoys fertile soil in sun or shade.
- Fruits are picked when ripe.
- Not normally grown in temperate climates.

Tamarind
Tamarindus indica

Family: Leguminosae
Description: semi-evergreen tropical tree
Ideal habitat: well-drained soil in the sun. Requires a hot climate
Part used: fruit

This complex fruit contains plant acids and volatile oils found in other herbs such as **mint** and **cinnamon**, as well as those found in lemons. The tamarind's flavour is sometimes described as sweet and sour. It has a pleasant aroma.

Originally from India, it was introduced to the West Indies during the 17th century, where it became an important ingredient in Indian cuisine. Tamarind is normally sold in a compressed block, although it is also available as dried slices, paste and as a concentrate.

USES

Culinary: an ingredient of Worcestershire sauce. The fruits can be eaten fresh or made into a drink. Used as a souring agent. If no tamarind is available, lemon juice is used as a poor substitute.

Medicinal: used as a laxative, externally it is used on sore eyes and ulcers.

Other: its over-ripe fruit was used to clean copper and brass.

CULTIVATION

- From seed in spring.
- From grafting in spring.
- Likes light, well-drained soil – minimum temperature of 15 °C (59 °F).
- Fruits are picked when ripe.

Tansy
Tanacetum vulgare

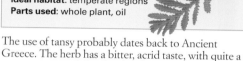

Family: Compositae/Asteraceae
Description: hardy perennial
Ideal habitat: temperate regions
Parts used: whole plant, oil

The use of tansy probably dates back to Ancient Greece. The herb has a bitter, acrid taste, with quite a pungent aroma. It is related to **feverfew** and **alecost**.

Tansy was used as part of the embalming procedure. The embalming sheets would be rubbed with the herb, as would the corpse itself, to protect it from earthworms. It was also used as a strewing herb.

USES

Culinary: the leaves can be added to desserts, but the practice is not recommended.
Medicinal: tansy tea applied externally can be used to treat scabies. Used internally to treat round and threadworms, but under medical supervision.
Other: leaves act as an insect repellent.

CULTIVATION

- From seed in spring or autumn.
- By division of roots in spring or autumn.
- Prefers well-drained soil in sun or partial shade.
- Best grown in a container to prevent it spreading all over the garden.
- Pick leaves as required.
- Pick flowers when open.

<table>
<tr><td>WARNING
Use only under medical supervision. Can induce menstruation or abortion. An overdose of tansy oil or tea may be fatal.</td></tr>
</table>

Tarragon
Artemisia dracunculus

Family: Compositae/Asteraceae
Alternative name: estragon
Description: half-hardy perennial
Ideal habitat: temperate regions
Parts used: leaf, oil

The species name is thought to be derived from the word 'dragon', for its strong and fiery flavour, or indeed its roots. It was also famed for its ability to heal bites from venomous creatures.

Tarragon was mixed with **fennel** to make drinks for the rulers of India.

USES

Culinary: the main ingredient of sauce béarnaise, but also added to other dishes with eggs and chicken. Used to flavour vinegars and oils.

Medicinal: not given to pregnant women. It has been used in aromatherapy to help digestive and menstrual problems.

Other: used in commercial flavourings, perfumes and detergents.

CULTIVATION
- From semi-ripe cuttings in summer.
- From division of established plants in spring.
- By division of root runners in spring or autumn.
- Cut back shrubby growth in spring if necessary and trim dead wood.

- Prefers warm, dry position, and may need protection in winter.
- Pick young leaves for vinegar, but otherwise pick as required.
- A very close relative known as Russian tarragon can be propagated from seed and is hardy.

Tea tree
Melaleuca alternifolia

Family: Myrtaceae
Description: evergreen tree, hardy if frost-free
Ideal habitat: well-drained soils, hot climate
Part used: oil

Tea tree probably obtained its name when Captain Cook used the leaf as a replacement for traditional teas when they were unavailable.

Rich in a volatile oil known as cineole, tea tree was widely used by Australian Aborigines. Later it was used by Australian soldiers during World War II to make dressings. It has powerful antiseptic, antifungal and antibacterial properties.

USES

Medicinal: applied externally to help prevent thrush and other common viral problems, as well as head lice. Must be diluted with a neutral oil or added to hot water. Can be used as a steam inhalation to relieve congestion.

Other: used in toiletries and in aromatherapy as a massage oil.

CULTIVATION

• From seed in spring.

• From semi-ripe cuttings in summer.

• Requires moist to wet soil with plenty of warmth and sun.

• The oil is distilled from leaves and twigs.

• Not normally grown in temperate regions but can be grown in a container pot, predominantly for the attractive foliage.

Thyme
Thymus vulgaris

Family: Labiatae/Lamiaceae
Description: evergreen hardy
   perennial
Ideal habitat: dry, stony,
   temperate regions
Parts used: whole plant,
   flowering top, oil

There are numerous types of thyme, of which common thyme is the most popular for both culinary and medicinal use. Like **bergamot**, it contains thymol, but also other important volatile oils, namely carvacol, linalol and cymol. The different thymes possess varying amounts of these volatile oils, which give each variety its distinctive character.

Thyme is a very aromatic herb, and all aromatic herbs are symbols of death. The souls of the dead were thought to rest in thyme. The smell of thyme has even been reported at places that are supposed to be haunted. The Egyptians used the oil for embalming and the Romans used it to help purify their rooms. Due to its antiseptic (and anti-fungal) properties, it was also used alongside **rosemary** to help prevent jail fever when prisoners were being brought before the judge.

WARNING

Do not take volatile oils internally except on prescription. Avoid if pregnant. The oil may cause dermatitis.

More romantically, thyme was carried by young women to help them reveal their true love. During the Middle Ages drinking a thyme tea was believed to help you to see fairies. More practically, thyme is a very good aid to digestion.

USES

Culinary: an ingredient of bouquet garni, used to flavour soups, stews and stuffings. Especially good for slow-cooked dishes as it holds its flavour well.

Medicinal: as a gargle or mouthwash for sore throats and gums. Also used for indigestion and coughs. Used externally for rheumatism.

Other: used in aromatherapy for aches, pains, exhaustion and depression. An ingredient of toothpaste and mouthwashes for its thymol content.

CULTIVATION

- From seed in spring.
- From softwood cuttings of new growth in early spring or summer.
- Requires poor, stony soil. Will withstand drought conditions but does not enjoy wet winters.
- Can be picked fresh throughout the year.
- If preserving thyme then pick before it flowers.

Turmeric
Curcuma domestica

Family: Zingiberaceae
Alternative names: haldi, kamin
Ideal habitat: hot, moist, tropical conditions
Part used: rhizome

Turmeric is one of the most common food flavourings and colourings in Asian cuisine. It might be regarded as a poor man's **saffron** as it has similar properties in terms of colour, taste and smell.

A symbol of fertility for Hindus, it would often be used as a paste in which a sacred thread could be dipped before being placed around the bride's neck. In Malaysia it was spread on the abdomen and umbilical cord of the mother who had just given birth, to ward off evil spirits. Many records exist referring to the use of turmeric in Chinese, Indian and Indonesian medicine.

USES

Culinary: an essential ingredient of curries and sauces, and a major ingredient of piccalilli. An ingredient of curry powder. Often used in butter and cheese.

Medicinal: research has shown that it is a good anti-inflammatory and liver-protective spice. Has been used for digestive and skin complaints and poor circulation. Used externally for injuries, sores and ringworm.

Other: used as the commercial food colouring E100. Also used as a dye.

CULTIVATION

• Propagate from last year's rhizomes which develop new shoots.

- Rhizomes can be harvested after about nine months when the plant is nearly 1 m (3 ft) high.
- The rhizomes are boiled, peeled and dried, losing about 75 per cent of their original weight.
- Not normally grown in temperate regions, but can be grown in a container pot, predominantly for its attractive foliage rather than its roots.

Valerian
Valeriana officinalis

Family: Valerianaceae
Alternative names: allheal, cat's valerian, cut finger, St George's herb
Description: hardy perennial
Ideal habitat: wetlands, temperate regions
Parts used: rhizome, root, oil

Valerian was used as long ago as 400 BC, and later by Anglo-Saxon herbalists. Its ability to cure many ailments prompted one of its old-fashioned names – 'allheal'. More recently it was used by soldiers in World Wars I and II to treat shell shock.

> **WARNING**
>
> Valerian should not be mixed with alcohol or sleeping tablets as it will increase the sedative effect.

The fresh roots have an unusual smell of stale leather, yet when dried smell rather like stale sweat. However, it is still used commercially in perfumes where musky smells are needed. The smell is attractive to both cats and rats, and it has been suggested that the Pied Piper of Hamelin carried the root. The herb itself is best described as bitter, with sedative properties.

USES

Medicinal: often used internally alongside **camomile**, **hops** and **passionflower** as a treatment for insomnia, hysteria, migraine and nervous indigestion.

Other: extracts used as food flavouring for baked goods, soft drinks, beers, tobacco and ice cream. Also used in bait for trapping wild cats and rodents.

CULTIVATION

- From seed in spring.
- By division of plant in autumn.
- Cut back after flowering in summer to prevent self-seeding.
- Enjoys rich, moist environment either in sun or shade.
- Dig up roots in autumn when plant is two to three years old, remove the fibrous roots and use the rhizome.

> **WARNING**
>
> Valerian's cousin, the red valerian *Valeriana ruber*, is poisonous in excess.

Vanilla
Vanilla plonifolia

Family: Orchidaceae
Description: tender ornamental epiphyte
Ideal habitat: tropical conditions
Part used: fruit (pod)

The Spaniards discovered the Aztecs in Mexico using this highly fragrant spice in the making of chocolate.

They brought it back to Europe, where it became an important food flavouring.

Vanilla is a climbing orchid, which produces flowers that open for one day only. It is pollinated by a species of bee and a long-beaked humming bird native to Mexico. Initially, efforts to grow vanilla elsewhere failed due to a lack of these natural 'pollinators', but the plant is now grown predominantely in Madagascar. The drying process is lengthy, which makes vanilla very expensive.

USES

Culinary: used in baking and for sweet dishes and confectionery.
Medicinal: attributed with aphrodisiac properties, but also used as a pick-me-up.
Other: used in perfumes and cosmetics.

CULTIVATION

- Propagate by cuttings at any time of the year.
- Must have moisture and compost with shade and humidity.
- The vine is usually encouraged to grow round trees.

- Bears fruit after three years and will continue to do so for twelve years.
- Pods are harvested unripe.

Vervain
Verbena officinalis

Family: Verbenaceae
Alternative name: verbena
Description: hardy perennial
Ideal habitat: prefers
    sunny, temperate
    regions
Part used: whole plant

Like **dill**, vervain was originally a native of the Mediterranean but was taken to numerous other countries by the Romans. Druids would make magic potions to purify Roman altars. The Ancient Greeks wore the herb.

Superstition has it that if you pick vervain you should bless it. Again, like dill, it is supposed to be a powerful protector against demons and disease.

> **WARNING**
> Avoid during pregnancy.

It is a bitter aromatic herb that is only used for medicinal purposes.

USES

Medicinal: used for nervous exhaustion and depression, and may be effective against migraines. Used in Chinese medicine as an antimalarial agent, and also for menstrual complaints, flu and feverish illnesses.

CULTIVATION

- From seed in spring.
- By division in autumn.
- Cut back flowers to prevent self-seeding.
- Prefers sunny, well-drained soil.
- Pick leaves as desired.

Violet
Viola odorata

Family: Violaceae
Description: hardy perennial
Ideal habitat: sheltered woodland,
    temperate regions
Parts used: leaf, flower, oil

Violet was the flower of Aphrodite, the goddess of love. However, there are many more stories relating violet to romance and love. One such Greek legend tells of Zeus falling in love with a beautiful maiden known as Io. Zeus turned Io into a cow to protect her from his jealous wife Juno and violets grew as food for Io.

Violets have always been revered for their perfume, and in the late 18th century a synthetic version of the volatile oil ionone was developed, which led to the demise of the violet market. Prior to this, violets were worn by all self-respecting women. The West Country's rail network was developed in response to the demand of the London market for violets grown in Devon.

The violet is sometimes described as 'cooling' due to its use in the treatment of fevers. It cleanses toxins from the body, and is believed to be antiseptic.

USES

Culinary: the flowers can be used in salads and as garnishes, and in ice creams and sweets. They can also be crystallised.

Medicinal: roots are used as an expectorant, while the plant's cooling nature is said to assist hangovers. A poultice helps sore and cracked nipples. Reputed to benefit benign and cancerous tumours. The flowers have sedative properties.

Other: use the flowers in potpourri. The oil is used in aromatherapy and for perfumes.

CULTIVATION

- From seed in autumn.
- From cuttings in spring.
- By division in summer.
- Prefers semi-shaded, moist, moderately heavy but rich soil.
- Pick leaves in early spring.
- Gather flowers when they open.

Wormwood
Artemisia absinthium

Family: Compositae/Asteraceae
Alternative names: absinthe, green ginger
Description: hardy perennial
Ideal habitat: prefers dry, well-drained, temperate regions
Part used: whole plant

Since Biblical times wormwood has been used for a number of purposes. It was hung on doors to repel evil spirits and used as a strewing herb. Added to ink the herb would prevent mice from eating old letters and documents. It also makes an effective household disinfectant.

Although a close relative of **tarragon**, wormwood is one of the most bitter herbs known. Historically it was used as an ingredient in many wines and tonics, but was eventually banned in the spirit absinthe as the volatile oil thujone was found to be addictive and to cause hallucinations.

Wormwood (artemisia absinthium)

USES

Medicinal: Used internally for treating worms, hence its name, and externally for bruises and bites.

Other: Can be used as a moth and insect repellent. Also used as a yellow dye.

CULTIVATION

- From seed in spring.
- By softwood cuttings in early summer.
- By semi-ripe cuttings in late summer.
- By division of established plants in autumn.
- Protect plants in temperatures below 5 °C (23 °F).

WARNING

Not to be taken internally unless medically supervised, habitual use can cause convulsions and vomiting. Pure oil is a strong poison.

- Prefers light, well-drained soils.
- Plant away from **dill** and **coriander** as the strong smell may affect their more delicate smell.
- Pick flowering tops as they open.
- Pick leaves for drying in summer.

Yarrow
Achillea millefolium

Family: Compositae/Asteraceae
Alternative name: millefoil
Description: hardy perennial
Ideal habitat: prefers dry, well-drained, temperate regions
Parts used: whole plant

Yarrow is a bitter but aromatic herb that was used by the Ancient Greeks to control bleeding. It is still prescribed today in herbal medicine. It is another herb that was felt to be magical and was used to ward off evil spirits. It also had romantic associations. A young girl would tickle her nose with the herb and if it bled it would show that her lover was not true to her.

Its Latin name is derived from the time when Achilles used yarrow during the Battle of Troy to help heal his warriors. Its anti-inflammatory action is likely to be due to the volatile oil azulene, the amount of which can vary from plant to plant even within the same area.

USES

Culinary: can be used in salads.

Medicinal: popular for fevers, high blood pressure, and to help prevent blood clots. Used externally on wounds, nose bleeds and haemorrhoids. Also used in Ayurvedic medicine.

Other: for composting, add a leaf to the compost mix and it will speed up the process. Infusions of yarrow will provide a copper-rich fertiliser.

CULTIVATION

- From seed in autumn.
- By division of established plants in spring and summer.
- Remove flowers to prevent self-seeding.
- Prefers dry, sandy soil.
- Difficult to eradicate due to long creeping roots, although the root secretions may increase the disease resistance of other plants. Yarrow itself does not become diseased or suffer from pests.
- Pick leaves as required.

WARNING

Can cause skin irritation and should not be used for prolonged periods. Not to be used by pregnant women.

THE HERB GARDEN

Choosing which herbs to grow

It does not matter what sort of garden area you own because there is such a wide variety of herbs. What is most important is that you choose the right plant for the conditions. A large proportion of herbs are Mediterranean in origin and therefore tend to prefer dry, sunny areas. However, there are some that are just as happy in shady, damp places. Growing plants in pots makes them easy to move around to a spot in which conditions are just right. Not all herbs are amenable to this, however.

Tender plants, which do not survive frosts, must be protected in winter, so it is important that there is somewhere for them to be overwintered in a frost-free environment. The perennial herbs can be grown in the same way as other flowers in borders or a rockery. Annual herbs can easily be grown in a vegetable garden. If you choose to do this, be sure to leave some of them to turn to seed since this will attract insects beneficial to the garden. The best herbs for this purpose are the *Umbelliferae* and *Labiatae* families, many of which are quite aromatic, for example mints, thymes and sages.

Some herbs do not like too many nutrients and prefer sunny, dry sites, which will often benefit from added sandstone chippings or sand which helps to improve drainage. Herbs that fall into this category tend to produce more essential oils in drought-like conditions. Examples include the thymes, bay, catmint and oregano.

The moisture-loving plants, such as mints, enjoy shade or dappled shade. It may also be necessary to dig in some well-rotted compost to help with moisture retention. Bergamot and lemon balm enjoy soil that does not dry out and will tolerate a little more sun. Horseradish and angelica also prefer a rich, damp soil but they must have sun.

It is often thought that herbs should be grown next to the kitchen door to enable the cook to have easy access to them, but some, such as lavender and nasturtium, are attractive as garden plants. Certain herbs can be grown indoors, too.

Growing herbs indoors is popular, and the more adventurous gardeners may like the challenge of some exotic plants that are more commonly seen in the tropics. Creative gardeners may prefer to plant herbs in a pattern, using edging plants to divide up the different groups of plants. Edging plants may also be used around the border to separate the plants. The herbs could be planted for colour or to make a picture, or even to spell out your name or that of a loved one. Designing a chequered pattern, or a wheel divided into segments, would both be simple methods of creating an interesting herb garden.

The possibilities are endless, but listed below are some ideas for groups of herbs that grow well together under particular conditions.

Common Culinary Herbs Suitable for Indoor Growing

Basil	Marjoram
Chives	Parsley
Coriander	Thyme

Herbs Suitable for Edging of a Border

Hyssop	Savory – winter
Lavender	Thyme – common variety
Oregano – golden variety	

Herbs Suitable for a Border

Angelica

Curry plant

Evening primrose

Garlic

Hops

Hyssop

Juniper

Lady's mantle

Lavender

Lemon balm

Liquorice

Mallow

Nigella

Poppy

Rosemary

Rue

Sage

St John's wort

Valerian

Wormwood

Herbs Suitable for Medicinal Uses

Camomile

Comfrey

Dill

Fennel

Feverfew

Heartsease

Garlic

Horseradish

Lavender

Lemon balm

Marigold

Meadowsweet

Mint

Passionflower

Rosemary

Thyme

Valerian

Herbs Suitable for a Culinary Herb Garden

Angelica
Basil
Bay
Blackcurrant
Borage
Caraway
Chervil
Chicory
Chives
Coriander
Dill
Fennel
Garlic
Horseradish
Hyssop
Lemon balm
Lovage

Marigold
Marjoram
Mint
Mustard
Nasturtium
Oregano
Parsley
Rosemary
Sage
Salad rocket
Savory – winter and summer
Sorrel
Sweet cicely
Tarragon
Thyme – lemon, common
Wild garlic

Lavender (lavendula augustifolia)

Herbs Suitable for Rockeries, Paved Paths and Patios

Catmint
Camomile
Chives
Curry plant
Feverfew
Heartsease

Marjoram
Mint (not all
  varieties)
Oregano
Pennyroyal
Red clover

Rosemary
  (prostrate
  varieties)
Violet
Strawberries
Savory

Herbs Suitable for Climbing

Honeysuckle
Jasmine
Passionflower

Herbs with Edible Flowers

Camomile
Chives
Heartsease
Nasturtium

Sage
Thyme
Violet

Chives (allium schenoprasum)

Herbs Suitable for Potpourri

Alecost
Bergamot
Camomile
Geranium – scented
Honeysuckle
Hyssop
Lavender

Lemon verbena
Mallow
Oregano
Rosemary
Sage – pineapple
Thyme – caraway
Thyme – orange-scented

Herbs Suitable for an Aromatic Garden

Alecost
Basil – sweet
Bergamot
Camomile
Chervil
Fennel
Geranium – scented
Hyssop
Jerusalem sage

Juniper
Lavender
Lemon balm
Marjoram – sweet
Oregano
Rosemary
Sweet rocket
Thyme

Herbs Suitable for Containers

Aloe
Bay
Camomile
Chillies
Chives
Coriander
Curry plant
Geranium
Heartsease
Juniper
Lady's mantle
Lavender

Lemon verbena
Marjoram
Mint
Nasturtium
Oregano
Parsley
Rosemary
Rue
Sage
Savory
Thyme

Tropical Herbs

Tropical herbs are not normally suitable for growing in the United Kingdom, as it is so difficult to create the right conditions for them to prosper. The following can be grown but may not reach their full height:

Aloe	Galangal	Lemon grass
Cardamom	Ginger	Turmeric

Tropical herbs not recommended for cultivation in the United Kingdom:

Allspice	Cloves	Saffron
Anise	Cumin	Sesame
Annatto	Mace	Star anise
Asafoetida	Mustard	Szechuan pepper
Cardamom	Nutmeg	Tamarind
Cassia	Papaya	Tea tree
Cinnamon	Pomegranate	Vanilla

Herbs Useful for their Insect-repelling Properties

Alecost	Garlic	Pennyroyal
Chives	Hyssop	Tansy
Fennel	Nasturtium	Wormwood
Feverfew	Nettle	

Growing herbs

Maintaining a herb garden is a relatively simple matter. Most herbs are wild plants and for that reason they are more tolerant than many modern cultivated plants.

Many herbs can be grown from seed. They may be grown in spring on a window ledge or in a greenhouse. It is best to give them compost with drainage, such as grit or perlite. The half-hardy perennials, such as basil and sweet marjoram, should be planted outside when all danger of frost has passed. Dill and angelica do not like to be disturbed so plant them where you want them to grow. Parsley may take time to germinate.

Mint, lemon balm, camomile and some thymes may be divided easily, but for the coloured varieties, such as golden thyme, taking cuttings may be the best option.

Take softwood cuttings in the early morning when the hormones are most concentrated. Select a vigorous non-flowering shoot with three or four pairs of leaves, trim the lower leaves, then cut the stem cleanly at the base where the leaves were. Place the stem in compost and cover with a plastic bag to maintain humidity. Keep out of direct sunlight. Catmint, feverfew, hyssop, lavender, rosemary, sage and winter savory are suitable for softwood cuttings. For semi-soft or hardwood cuttings, cut a little later in the plant's growth.

Red clover (trifolium pratense)

Drying herbs

Pick herbs on a warm, sunny day after the dew has dried and before the plant flowers; this will maximise their flavour. Dry upside down in a dark, airy place. The faster they dry the better, as they retain more of their aromatic oils. Keep the different herbs away from each other as their flavours may mingle. Seeds can be collected by placing the almost ripe head in a paper bag; as they dry the seeds pop out and can easily be collected.

Freezing herbs

Some herbs, such as chives, dill, fennel, parsley and tarragon, are better frozen. Pick the herbs, wash and clean, shaking them dry. Place them in a plastic bag, and then into a container so they do not get damaged. Alternatively, chop the herbs and place them in an ice cube tray; each ice cube slot will hold roughly one tablespoon of chopped herbs and one teaspoon of water.

Single leaves or flowers can also be put into ice cube trays and frozen to make attractive ice cubes for cocktails.

Herb tinctures

These are medicinal liquid substances which are distinguishable from herbal infusions by the fact that they are preserved in alcohol. This means that they keep for longer than infusions. In addition, tinctures are often more concentrated than infusions.

For 500 ml (1 pint) use 100 g (3½ oz) dried herbs or 150 g (5¼ oz) fresh herbs and 500 ml (1 pint) vodka.

- Mix the herbs and vodka together.
- Shake the mixture thoroughly twice a day and store in a cool, dark place.
- Strain the herbs out, squeezing to ensure the volatile oils are extracted.
- Store in a dark bottle.
- Use one teaspoon per glass of water.

Herbs Suitable for Tinctures

Fennel	Rosemary
Liquorice	St John's wort
Passionflower	

Herb infusions

For each cup use one teaspoon of dried or two teaspoons of fresh herbs.

- Cover with boiling water and leave to stand for 10 minutes to infuse.
- Strain off the herbs.
- Add honey to taste.
- The infusion can be refrigerated for up to 24 hours.

Herbs Suitable for Infusions

Bergamot	Lemon balm
Borage	Lemon grass
Caraway	Mint – especially
Camomile	peppermint
Chervil	Parsley
Dandelion	Passionflower
Elder	Red clover
Evening primrose –	Rosemary
leaves	Rue
Fennel	Sage
Ginger	St John's wort
Honeysuckle – flowers	Thyme
Hops – female flower	Valerian – roots
Lady's mantle	Yarrow

Using spices

Select whole spices where possible as they tend to keep their flavour for longer. Fresh roots such as ginger and galangal have different flavours from the dried version, as does lemon grass.

Some spices should be dry fried to improve their flavour. This is very common in Indian cookery where the spices are roasted in a heavy-bottomed pan for 2 to 3 minutes, shaking the pan to prevent them from burning. They are then ground. Also typical of Indian cookery is frying the spices whole in oil before the rest of the ingredients are added.

If ground spices are required, it is best to grind them just before they are needed using a pestle and mortar or a small coffee grinder. Ginger and nutmeg are often grated using a fine grater. Berries and cardamoms can be crushed using a pestle and mortar or by using a rolling pin and putting the herbs between sheets of greaseproof paper. Ginger and makrut leaves can be sliced, or the makrut leaves may be shredded or torn and added as required to the dish. Tamarind pulp can be infused in warm water for 10 minutes and mixed with the fingers to loosen the purée from the seeds before straining and using the juice in cooking.

Herb and spice oils

Use a minimum of four teaspoons of herb leaves (no stalks) and 500 ml (1 pint) of oil, e.g. sunflower or olive oil.

- Crush the leaves to release the oils (use a pestle and mortar or the bowl of a spoon in a dish).
- Add some oil and crush again. Continue to do this until all the oil has been used.
- Pour into a jar and seal.
- Place the jar on a windowsill.
- Shake every other day.
- After two weeks, strain through muslin into the final bottle, and add a couple of leaves for decoration.

Herbs and Spices Suitable for Oils

Basil
Cinnamon
Coriander – seeds and
    leaves
Dill
Fennel
Garlic – use bulbs
Lemon grass

Lime leaves
Mixed herbs – of your
    choice
Oregano
Rosemary
Sage
Thyme – lemon

Herb and spice vinegars

These are made in much the same way as the herb and spice oils, but the vinegar (either cider or white wine vinegar should be used) must be warmed before it is added to the herbs.

Both oils and vinegars may be used in cooking for an almost limitless number of dishes. Oils may also be used for massage.

Herbs and Spices Suitable for Vinegars

Basil	Ginger
Chervil	Lemon balm
Chillies	Mint
Chives	Oregano
Coriander – seeds	Rosemary
Dill – seeds and leaves	Savory
Fennel – seeds and	Tarragon
leaves	Thyme
Garlic	

Aromatherapy

Aromatherapy is an increasingly well-respected and widely practised form of complementary medicine. It can relieve tension, assist with minor ailments and, alongside conventional medicine, help to ease the symptoms of major complaints such as cancer. The essential oils used in aromatherapy are extracted from berries, leaves and flowers.

Massage – add four or five drops of oil to each 10 ml of carrier oil; almond and grape seed oil are the most popular.

Burning – add a few drops of oil to a small amount of water, then add to a vaporiser to freshen rooms and lift the mood.

Baths – add four or five drops of oil to running water. Dilute the essential oil with carrier oil for babies and young children.

APPENDICES

Glossary

aromatherapy – the use of essential oils for cosmetics or the treatment of medical problems.

Ayurvedic medicine – derived from Sanskrit, meaning 'the science of life', Indian in origin and dating back 5,000 years. The basis of today's homeopathy.

bolt/bolting – the premature production of flowers and seeds by a plant.

bouquet garni – a collection of culinary herbs traditionally wrapped together in muslin and added to savoury dishes to add flavour, the bouquet garni is removed before the food is served.

Chinese medicine – herbal medicine used throughout history by the Chinese.

Culpeper – author of the *English Physician* in 1652. This book provided advice on treating the ailments of the day.

cuttings – hardwood: taken from mature wood at the end of the growing season.

cuttings – softwood: taken from young, immature non-flowering stems.

deadheading – removal of flower heads after flowering; this helps to produce more flowers.

dividing – the splitting of roots to produce separate plants.

everlasting flowers – flowers that after picking display no obvious signs of dying. Ideal for dried-flower arrangements or for use as decoration.

expectorant – a substance which encourages the removal of phlegm.

flavanoids – group of chemical compounds which benefit the body in a similar way to vitamins but are not essential to the body's functioning in the way that vitamins are.

fortifying oil – an oil thought in the past to have beneficial properties.

Gerard – author of one of the first books cataloguing plants. The book also served as a useful record of how to grow and use herbs.

hardy perennial – a plant that will last for several years.

hardy/half-hardy plant – a plant intolerant of cold temperatures, i.e. below freezing point.

hybrid – the result of crossing two distinctly different plants.

jail fever – also gaol fever, the sicknesses and illnesses that ravaged prisoners in dirty, dark, damp, crowded jails.

layering – where a stem is encouraged to grow roots by making a small cut on the underside of the stem. This is then buried in soil.

mulch – the spreading of a substance such as dead leaves, pine needles, sawdust or even plastic to help protect the soil from weeds and to prevent water loss. May also provide nutrients to the soil.

overwinter – keeping a plant out of the frost to prevent it from dying during the winter period.

self-seeding – refers to seeds from the plant that germinate and grow very easily.

setting seeds – the drying of seeds on the flower head.

strewing – the spreading of aromatic herbs to sweeten the air.

tender perennial – a plant which will last for several years, but cannot withstand frost and has to be over-wintered.

thymol – an oil found in some herbs and used in oral preparations. Has an antiseptic and fungicidal effect.

turn to seed – refers to plants which flower easily and develop seeds if leaves are not picked regularly.

volatile oils – aromatic plant oils which can be extracted or isolated from plants.

Further reading

Brown, D., *Encyclopaedia of Herbs*, The Royal Horticultural Society, Dorling Kindersley, 1995.

McVicar, J., *Jekka's Complete Herb Book*, Kyle Cathie Limited, 1994.

Morris, S. and Mackley, L., *The Cook's Encyclopaedia of Spices*, Lorenz Books, 1997.

Search, G., *The Healing Garden*, BBC Books, 2001.

Van Straten, M., *Superboosters: Herb, Plant and Spice Extracts to Boost Health*, Mitchell Beazley, 2000.

Wildwood, C., *The Encyclopaedia of Healing Plants,* Piatkus, 1999.

Index of
alternative names

Honeysuckle (lonicera caprifolium)